Contents

Earthquake in Lisbon

Portugal was hit by Europe's largest earthquake on 1st November, 1755. The magnitude of the quake was probably about 8.7. The shaking demolished many buildings in the capital city, Lisbon. The harbour was smashed by giant sea waves which arrived about an hour after the shaking. Some 60 000 people were killed, either by collapsing buildings or in the sea waves. It was a religious festival that day, and the quake happened at 9.30 am local time. Throughout Europe at that very hour many people were in churches, the tallest buildings of the time. Well beyond the limit of felt shaking, church chandeliers were noticed to be swaying; later it was realised this was an effect of the distant Lisbon earthquake.

Effects in Lisbon

Within Lisbon, fires broke out in private houses and churches, and merged to a single fire-storm which took three days to burn out. At 11.00 am there was an aftershock. This caused the collapse of buildings which were still standing but had already been severely weakened by the main shock. Yet more people died, many in the church of Sao Paolo, where the homeless and wounded were sheltering after the earlier main shock.

1 Many masonary buildings in Lisbon collapsed in the earthquake; some, like this cloister of the Mosteiro dos Jerónimos, survived.

Effects on European Society

Europeans of the time were profoundly distressed by this destruction of a great city, a place rich in palaces and art treasures. There had been a general religious belief that God would not allow a calamity such as this. After the event, many people thought and wrote in terms of divine anger, and interpreted the earthquake as a divine punishment of the inhabitants of Lisbon.

This was a time when scientific thought was beginning to have influence in at least some corners of society. But still, there was no general understanding of earthquakes, or of many other natural events. The Lisbon quake triggered the thinkers of the time to try to explain earthquakes in a non-religious context.

The philosopher, Jean-Jacques Rousseau, suggested that if only people would return to the natural state of living in open spaces, rather than among the crowded buildings of cities, then earthquakes would not harm them.

This sound but impractical advice has been found to be inappropriate in social terms. The centuries since then have seen huge population expansion globally, along with the increase of urban areas.

Birth of modern earthquake science

A British engineer, John Michell, wrote after the Lisbon quake that the shaking was waves resulting from rock that had been moved.

He believed that the speed of travel of the earthquake waves could be measured, and after interviewing witnesses to the Lisbon quake, he suggested a speed of 500 metres per second which turned out to be a gross underestimate. This came about because in 1755, there was no way of transmitting a universal time. Clocks and watches could only be synchronised when they were seen by the same person at the same time, leading to variations in time-keeping from one village or town to another. Inevitably Michell's calculations included the unintentional inaccuracies passed onto him by his witnesses.

Giant sea waves

The earthquake originated 300 kilometres offshore from Portugal on the ridge of seamounts that extends towards Madeira. About twenty minutes after the main shock, the sea waves (tsunami) arrived, killing even more people than those crushed in the falling buildings. Ships at harbour were smashed by waves which brought water inland to ten metres above normal high tide level. The effects of the sea waves were noticed later that day way beyond Portugal itself, on the Cornwall coast of the English Channel.

In the morning, water levels of lakes and docks far from Lisbon were seen to bob up and down as the fading earthquake shock waves passed. In Portsmouth docks in southern England, water levels fluctuated over a few minutes, and in Scandinavia and Scotland, lake levels were disturbed. Since the shaking was imperceptible to people such distances away, the observers were very puzzled.

Portsmouth

Cornwall

area of
earthquake
effects

2 Earthquake shaking caused damage to buildings over the area shaded red, but the effects were noticed throughout Europe, in the area shaded yellow.

• Lisbon

epicentre

area of earthquake
damage in red

3 In this engraving, tidal waves are shown engulfing Lisbon harbour, whilst buildings in the city are collapsing.

1906 San Francisco

One of the largest and most famous of all earthquakes is the San Francisco earthquake of 1906. Its magnitude was 8.3, and it struck the city at 5.13 am local time on 18th April. At 1906 values, the damage was estimated at $500 million. The official death toll was only 700, a very low figure considering this was such a large quake affecting a major city, and that it happened at a time when people were indoors.

Fire followed the shaking

Many of the city buildings, especially homes, were built of wood. Being more flexible than masonry, these wooden buildings probably survived the shaking quite well, allowing people to escape. However, the shaking was followed by fire, which laid the city to waste. Underground water pipes had been disrupted by the shaking, so there was no way the fire could be slowed, other than by dynamiting whole blocks of houses to make fire breaks. Eventually the fire burnt itself out.

Death toll

Possibly more people died in 1906 than the official death toll of 700; some bodies may have been incinerated totally in the burning houses, and may thus have escaped being officially recorded.

1 Whole districts of San Francisco went up in flames.

Buildings destroyed

Damage to buildings was especially concentrated on the waterfront. Here the land had been extended into the bay, as made ground. In the years before the earthquake, the made-up ground had already been subsiding, as its groundfill material settled and became more compacted. During the earthquake, shaking was amplified by these soft materials, and the groundfill itself became more thoroughly compacted. As a result, the ground surface had a new profile after the shaking had died away. Waterfront buildings were severely distorted, even though some of the buildings themselves might have been constructed in a way which could have tolerated earthquake shaking alone.

San Francisco

intensity of shaking dies out rapidly with distance

Pacific Ocean

2 The most intense shaking was confined to the west coast of California. For such a large earthquake, the shaking was felt over a relatively small region.

Intense shaking

The area of felt shaking extended across California into Nevada and Oregon, not a huge area for such a large earthquake. The rocks in the region are relatively soft, as they have been shattered and deformed by many earthquakes through millions of years. Such soft rocks absorb earthquake shock waves, limiting the severe shaking to a small area.

1906 San Francisco

Beginnings of a legend

This was the first major quake to hit the American west since the region had become urbanised. In the previous century, earthquakes had shaken a sparsely-populated landscape when there were few buildings and no cities. The San Francisco earthquake has taken its place along with many other frontier stories, all relating to the huge westward migration of people across the continent. The 1970s' film *Earthquake* updated this earthquake legend, and showed many of the hazards and dilemmas that the people of California might have to face again.

3 This steel frame building was in the process of construction at the time the earthquake struck. The steel frame was unharmed. Fire gutted the timber floors of the masonry building in front, allowing the rear walls to collapse, while the more substantially built frontage remained intact.

4 Publicity poster for the film, *Earthquake*.

1923 Kanto

On 1st September 1923, at two minutes before noon, the largest Japanese earthquake for a century shook Tokyo and the surrounding plain. As many as 143 000 people are thought to have died, some in collapsing houses and other structures, while others were suffocated or burned to death in the fire-storm that followed the earthquake.

1 Most of Japan is mountainous, with steep slopes; people live in the flat valleys.

Elements of a catastrophe

Three quarters of the population of Japan live on the one quarter of the land which is flat, where rice paddies and tea plantations separate huge cities. In 1923, before the earthquake, two million people lived in Tokyo alone. One reason why so many people were killed in this earthquake was the density of the population in the region where shaking was most intense.

Another reason why so many people died is the instability of the land itself. Tokyo and the neighbouring city of Yokohama, then as now, are built on flat land in Tokyo Bay, land that is made of soft sediments that have been accumulating over the last few million years. The harbour areas of both cities are built on land reclaimed from the sea. Such soft sediment and reclaimed land may be seriously disrupted during earthquake shaking. They may even liquefy and become like quicksand as water is squeezed out. Large or heavy buildings situated on this land may sink into the ground or topple over.

2 Yokohama Harbour after the 1923 earthquake. The harbour structure sank unevenly as the reclaimed land that it was built on liquefied.

The fire storm

It is estimated that 38 000 people died in the fires that followed immediately after the earthquake. The midday meal was being prepared in thousands of homes, and cooking was by oil, or on open fires. Whilst today steel-framed, concrete blocks of offices and flats pervade the Tokyo skyline, at that time, most people lived in traditional-style Japanese houses made of wood. Although such houses may have withstood the earthquake shaking well, they caught fire easily, catching light from the overturned hot oil and naked fires.

So many houses burned that there was not enough oxygen left to breathe, even in the parks where thousands of citizens fled to escape the fires. These people were suffocated. Others were burned alive by the intense heat of the fires. The heat caused air to rush in from outside the city, fanning the flames, resulting in a great whirlwind of fire. Homes, libraries, palaces and irreplaceable art treasures went up in the flames.

3 Whole housing districts were reduced to heaps of rubble by the fire. Houses, which were made of wood and furnished with paper and fine rice-straw *tatami* mats, fed the fire.

Earthquakes in Japan

This very large earthquake, of magnitude 8.3, affected the whole of the Kanto Plain around Tokyo, giving the event its official title, the Kanto earthquake. As well as liquefaction and superficial ground cracks, it caused permanent distortions of the ground surface, uplifting or offsetting some regions by as much as two metres. In the Kanto plain, there are many examples of previous earthquakes having caused similar amounts of ground level change.

These earlier events can be dated, and they show the history of previous great earthquakes. It seems that similar size events take place at intervals which average out at one in every 500 years, in the years 33, 818, 1755 and 1923AD.

A somewhat smaller earthquake, of about magnitude 7, shook Tokyo in 1855, and this has led to the idea that Tokyo's largest earthquakes happen every 70 years. On this basis, the 1990s is 'time' for another large earthquake. This might not be as large as the 1923 event, but even a smaller quake could be devastating for Tokyo and the other Kanto Plain cities and their inhabitants.

5 Map showing the region of Japan affected by the 1923 Kanto earthquake.

KANTO PLAIN

Tokyo

Yokohama

epicentre

Pacific Ocean

4 Interior of a traditional Japanese house built of wood. Paper-paned wood screens separate rooms, the floor is covered with rice-straw mats.

1988 *Spitak, Armenia*

Shockingly large numbers of people were killed, injured or made homeless in this magnitude 6.8 earthquake. It happened at 11.41 am local time, on 7th December 1988 in the mountainous border country between Turkey and what was then the USSR. Many buildings collapsed because the individual building components fell apart. People were buried and crushed under concrete floors and wall panels which parted company without breaking; the buildings fell as if they were made of giant playing cards.

Caspian Sea

Black Sea

Spitak

Leninakan

Lake Sevan

intensity of shaking dies out with distance

Unsuitable buildings

Many modern buildings in towns like Leninakan had been constructed in a hurry during rapid population growth in this earthquake-prone region. Large blocks of flats had been constructed, with concrete floor and ceiling panels merely resting against walls without being properly tied to the rest of the building. There was no possibility that these buildings could withstand earthquake shaking.

1 Intense damage was confined to a small area, and affected the cities of Spitak and Leninakan.

Older buildings

In Leninakan, some apartment houses and town houses which were already a century old survived the shaking with only minor damage. These buildings were made of volcanic rock which was held together by good mortar made of the local pozzolan earth, also volcanic in origin.

The terrible toll of this earthquake in deaths and destruction to property clearly shows up the danger posed by unsuitable buildings. Old buildings had been built to high quality; they were made of sound quality stone, and were held together with good mortar. Some tolerated the shaking

in 1988 reasonably, and may well have survived several previous earthquakes. Modern buildings, hurriedly thrown together from slabs of reinforced concrete, without adequate regard or proper allowance for the possibility of earthquakes, fell apart.

Aftermath

In total, 500 000 people were made homeless. The dead numbered 25 000, while 13 000 were injured. Many people were rescued, alive but injured, from the heaps of concrete slabs. Since the massive slabs had interlocked as the buildings collapsed, they could not be lifted without the aid of heavy machinery, so rescue had to wait till thousands of cranes, bulldozers and excavators were brought into Leninakan. Usually after earthquakes, few people survive in fallen buildings for longer than three days. But, even after the third day in the depth of the winter cold at Leninakan, 7000 people were rescued alive.

Major traffic jams were caused by the need to transport 60 000 civil defence aid workers into the affected area, as well as the slow-moving lifting and digging machinery. In addition, 120 000 homeless people were moved out to temporary housing elsewhere. In this mountainous area, roads were disrupted by landslides which had been triggered by the earthquake shaking. This increased the existing problems of moving so many vehicles and people.

3 People became trapped between the heavy concrete floor slabs of some modern high-rise buildings.

2 Some traditional buildings escaped with relatively little damage.

4 Concrete slab buildings fell inwards; the individual sections had not been adequately tied together.

9

A *fault breaks...*

The rocky surface of the Earth is cut by millions of fractures, known to geologists as ***faults***; each fault marks a place where an earthquake once originated. Along some of these faults, earthquakes may recur again and again. Faults are especially numerous in places where the Earth's surface is or has been under a lot of stress, for example in mountainous regions.

How rocks fracture

The outer surface of the Earth shifts in response to movements within its interior. This causes stress to build up over some surface regions. To begin with, rock distorts, and some tiny cracks may open up along the stress directions. Eventually, as stress continues to build up, there comes a stress level which the rock can no longer tolerate. The rock suddenly tears apart; it fractures, and vibrational energy spreads out from the point of rupture. After the fault has ruptured, most of the stress has been released.

It may be that once a fault has broken, it is reactivated again and again, in earthquake after earthquake. This means the breaking surface has become the weakest part of the rock. Another possibility is that existing faults could seal up and become stronger than surrounding rock; then, later earthquakes in the same area take place along new fault surfaces. In this way, there can be groups of faults which are related to each other.

Evidence of recent earthquakes is sometimes visible at the Earth's surface, where fences or walls are displaced or a new, small cliff appears. The amount that the rocks slip in an earthquake is a fraction of a metre to, at most, several metres. When the same fault moves time and time again in the same direction, the total displacement could mean that natural features like rivers become diverted.

Often, after an earthquake occurs, the new position of the rocks is still unstable. Further smaller earthquakes, called aftershocks, occur until the rocks settle down into a stable position. This usually takes days or weeks, or even months, depending on the size of the earthquake fault.

1 Within the width of this fault, rock is crunched to small fragments.

2 A computer image of a 50 kilometres-long fault. The colour fringes show up variations in strain within the rocks around the fault.

Types of faults *(see right)*

Sometimes the rocks at the surface are being pulled apart, at other times they are being compressed. Sometimes there is a shearing, sideways movement. Most often, in nature, there is some sideways movement along with either compression or stretching.

3 A set of sedimentary rock layers cut by a fracture.

4 The rock layers are displaced and stretched by a *normal fault*.

5 The rock layers are displaced by a *reverse fault* in an area of compression.

6 Lateral faulting goes with sideways movement. This fault is sometimes called a *wrench fault*, a *strike-slip fault* or a *transcurrent fault*.

7 A reverse fault which has a low angle is called a thrust or *thrust fault*.

8 **How rocks fracture.** Rocks are *elastic*.

They become deformed before they fracture.

The deformed areas of rock snap back into an undeformed state after the rock has fractured.

...and seismic waves spread out

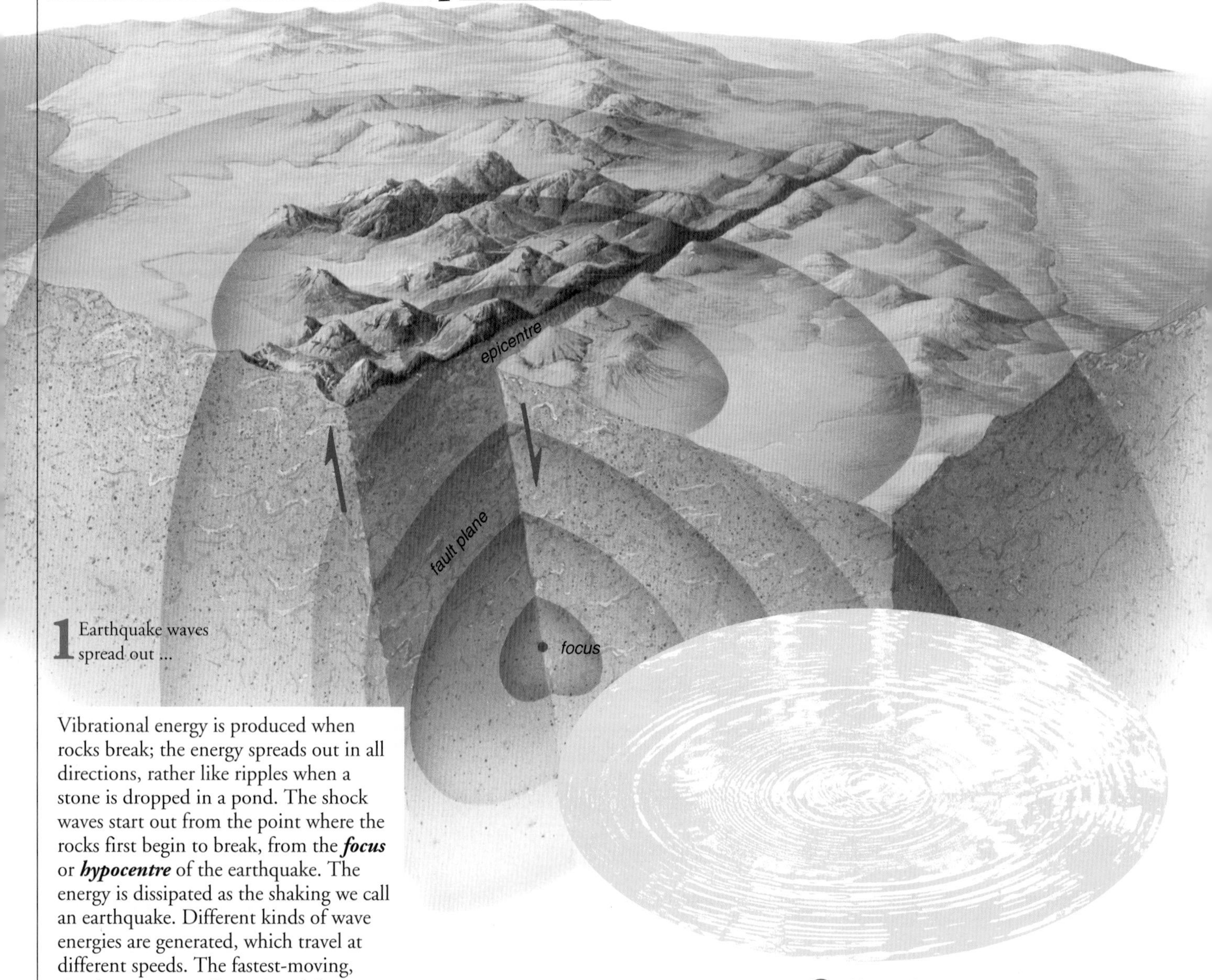

epicentre

fault plane

focus

1 Earthquake waves spread out ...

Vibrational energy is produced when rocks break; the energy spreads out in all directions, rather like ripples when a stone is dropped in a pond. The shock waves start out from the point where the rocks first begin to break, from the *focus* or *hypocentre* of the earthquake. The energy is dissipated as the shaking we call an earthquake. Different kinds of wave energies are generated, which travel at different speeds. The fastest-moving, simplest waves are *P-waves*, while *surface waves* travel the most slowly.

2 ...like ripples on a pond.

3 P-waves.

P-waves travel fastest. Like sound waves, they are a series of compressions, with spacings-out in between. Particles of rock vibrate in the same direction as the waves are travelling. P-waves travel through solid rocks, through liquids like the ocean water or molten rock, and also can be transmitted into air, where they travel as an audible, low, rumbling, sound wave.

Like runners in a marathon

Near the *epicentre*, shaking lasts just as long as the rock is breaking, seconds, or maybe minutes in a large earthquake. As waves travel away from the focus of the quake, so the wave energy gets spread out in time, like runners in a marathon race who all start out at the same time, but get spread out over the route because some run faster than others. In earthquakes, even though rupture only takes tens of seconds, the waves recorded at a distant site may take over an hour to pass by; they have become spread out over the distance they have travelled.

4 S-waves.

S-waves travel about half as fast as P-waves. As the waves pass through rock, individual rock particles are vibrated in a direction at right angles to the direction the waves are travelling.

This diagram shows only two directions of vibration, one horizontal and the other vertical. In reality, vibration is in all directions in this plane. S-waves travel through solids, but cannot travel through air or through liquids (page 22).

The speed of all seismic waves depends on the density of the rocks they pass through. They travel fastest in denser rocks, and faster as they travel through deeper levels of the Earth. As a rough guide, P-waves travel at about eight kilometres a second. S-waves travel about 4.6 kilometres a second, while surface waves are the slowest travelling about 3.6 kilometres a second.

5 Surface waves.

Surface waves travel slower than S-waves. Their motion is a complex rolling. Like waves on the sea, the maximum energy is concentrated at the surface, and dies out with depth.

Surface waves take some time and distance to develop, so they tend to be inconspicuous near the epicentre of the earthquake, while further away from this centre, they may be the main cause of felt shaking and damage. Close to the epicentre of an earthquake, P-waves and S-waves are more likely to be the cause of felt shaking.

The birth of seismology

Old Chinese manuscripts show that eighteen hundred years ago, a Chinese thinker was puzzled enough by earthquakes to build an apparatus to register shaking. For the next sixteen hundred years though, there seems to have been little scientific interest in measuring earthquakes, though a few people in earthquake-affected regions attempted to register the strength of shocks with simple devices, such as delicately balanced objects which were overturned by the onset of shaking. The 18th century saw the beginnings of systematic earthquake-measuring devices.

Zhang Heng, China

The huge region of China is shaken by many earthquakes. Before the invention of telegraph and telephone, news of a quake which happened in a far corner of the ancient empire could take days or even weeks to arrive at the emperor's palace in the capital. The sage Zhang Heng, in AD 132, invented a device which could show that a distant earthquake had happened only seconds or minutes ago. An instrument of this sort, which shows that an earthquake has happened, is a *seismoscope*.

Earthquake House, Scotland

A series of earthquakes in Comrie, Scotland, between 1839 and 1846, was studied by a group of scientists, a committee of the British Association for the Advancement of Science. To detect the earthquakes, James Forbes invented an instrument based on an inverted pendulum, using an engineering principle that is still used to detect earthquakes today. Several of these instruments were installed around Comrie. The committee called their instrument a seismometer, although by modern definitions, it is really only a seismoscope, because it did not record the time of of the quake.

The Committee lapsed in the mid eighteen-forties but was revived when the earthquakes intensified once more around 1870. The first ever purpose-built seismological observatory was put up in 1874 at Comrie, to house another kind of seismoscope, based on wooden rods. In time, the earthquakes died away, and the observatory, Earthquake House, became derelict. It has recently been restored and is open to the general public.

2 Earthquake House in Comrie, Scotland.

Palmieri's seismograph

A device that can show the time that a shock occurred is called a *seismograph*. The first was devised by Luigi Palmieri, in Italy in 1856, to record earthquakes which accompanied eruptions of the nearby volcano, Vesuvius.

1 Model of Zhang Heng's apparatus: the dragon's heads around the outside of the great bronze urn held metal balls, one of which would drop into a toad's mouth when there was an earthquake. Which dragon's mouth released its grip indicated the direction of the earthquake.

3 Milne's Twin-Boom seismograph.

Seismometers

An instrument that can record the time, and accurately measure the ground motion is called a *seismometer*. All seismometers operate on variations of the pendulum principle which had been used at Comrie. The early development of seismometers is largely due to John Milne, a mining engineer, who taught geology in Japan from 1876 to 1895. Milne realised the need to have many recording stations in different places in order to understand earthquake shaking.

On his return to Britain, Milne set up an observatory on the Isle of Wight, which became the world centre of seismology up until his death in 1913. His seismometer was improved by John Shaw, an amateur seismologist. Many instruments of the Milne-Shaw type were installed at observatories around the world; some were still in service in recent decades. The ability to accurately measure ground motion, and to record earthquakes all around the world, opened up the potential of seismology enormously. Much of our modern understanding of the nature of the Earth and its interior stems from the scientific advances that were made possible by Milne's work.

4 John Milne.

Most of this understanding was painstakingly worked out by brain power and slide rule or calculator, taking months or years even. It was done from reading seismograms which had been recorded by pen on paper, or scratched onto smoked paper, or were photographically recorded.

5 The Milne seismometers worked on the principle of a swinging heavy pendulum (below). The heavy pendulum stays stationary while the ground below is shaken by an earthquake. A pen attached to the pendulum mass writes a wiggly line as the record of the earthquake. Three instruments, each at right angles, are used to give the fullest record of the shaking.

Modern earthquake recording methods

The seismological apparatus of Milne's day was large and cumbersome. Through the 20th century, the trend has been towards smaller and more sophisticated seismometers. The everyday life of seismologists has been transformed by technological advances in electronics and the possibilities offered by computer analysis, so that nowadays it is possible to process recordings within minutes or hours, and learn more and more about how and why earthquakes happen.

Modern seismometers

Although modern seismometers work on the same basic principle as that in older instruments, they are much more compact. In place of Milne's swinging pendulum, a modern instrument has a weight attached to a spring. Earthquake vibrations cause the weight to try to move relative to the rest of the instrument, but electromagnets hold it in place. The varying amount of current required by the electromagnets is recorded, and is a measure of the amplitude of the ground motion.

Seismological networks

Modern instruments are small and rugged, so can easily be deployed at many locations around the countryside. Each individual seismometer is placed in a pit, preferably on solid rock, and is linked to a radio transmitter mast. Power is provided from a solar panel placed above the pit. Connected together by computer, such a network can record even the smallest earthquakes.

The recording each instrument makes is digital, like the information on musical compact discs. The digital information from each seismometer in the network is transmitted by the radio link to a central computer, where it is analysed by the computer software under the expert eye of a seismologist. Earthquake signals are identified among the many other types of vibrations which are recorded, such as passing traffic, quarry blasts and sonic booms. Signals from the network can be called up to a computer screen, where the data can be analysed directly.

For large, distant or specially interesting earthquakes, the data can be shared with other seismologists around the world almost immediately using the international computer network.

Easy by network

A linked network of seismometers can be used to give clearer detail about earthquakes as well as greater accuracy. The spacing of the instruments can be tailored to the type of event that is being measured. Networks can monitor the regional pattern of earthquakes over a few hundred square kilometres. A more densely spaced network of recording instruments allows very small events to be analysed in detail. Over tens of square kilometres, they are used to map the small earth tremors which can be used to predict the progress of volcanic eruptions. A closely-spaced network can even resolve the small rockbursts and collapses from old underground mining operations.

1 Part of a seismic monitoring network in central Scotland, showing the outstations (seismometers), receiving station and a small local earthquake.

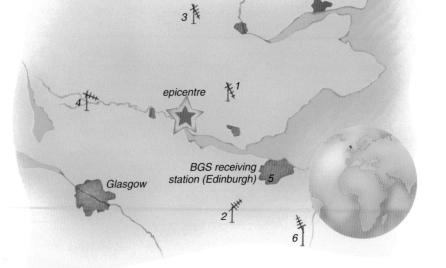

Modern earthquake recording methods

2 Solar panel and transmitter aerial at one of the outstations.

3 The central receiving station for the network, at the British Geological Survey in Edinburgh.

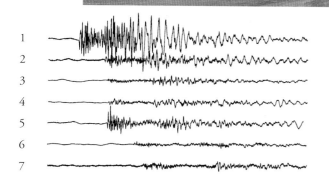

5 Seismograms of the Scottish earthquake shown left. Station No.1 receives the signal first and records the biggest amplitudes.

4 A British Geological Survey seismologist calls up the records on a computer screen.

17

Reading a seismogram

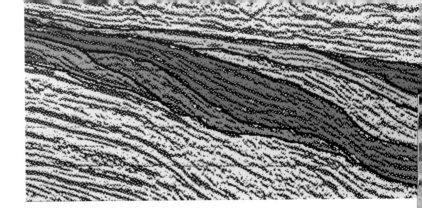

Seismograms contain rich and varied information about processes that occur in an earthquakes. They also contain information about the rocks they have passed through on the way from the earthquake to the seismometer where they are recorded. The skill of the seismologist lies in separating out each scrap of information from the whole mass of data for each event, and then interpreting the results.

1 Part of a seismic profile showing layers of sediments in a sedimentary basin. The horizontal distance is about 20 kilometres.

Locating an earthquake

A seismologist distant from an earthquake wants to know where the event happened. By looking at the records from several different recording stations at once, it is possible to find out from which direction the earthquake waves came. The recording station closest to the event picks up the signals first, and they arrive last at the one the furthest away.

Finding the distance

A seismogram shows up the arrival times of the first P-waves and S-waves at its recording station. The two types of waves become separated out in time because P-waves travel about twice as fast as S-waves. Nearby earthquakes show only a small separation in arrival time between these two sets of waves. The further away the station is from the earthquake, the more separated out in time the two types of waves become. The amount of time that elapsed between the arrival of the first P-waves and the first S-waves can be converted from minutes and seconds into kilometres, to give the distance from the epicentre.

Working out the magnitude

Dropping a pebble in a pond makes small waves. Dropping in a large boulder makes bigger waves. In the same way, small earthquakes make seismic waves with small amplitude, but seismic waves from large earthquakes have greater amplitude. The amplitude can be read from seismograms, but that is not enough to determine the size. It is important to know how far away the quake is as well. The further away the earthquake, the smaller the amplitude will be, because earthquake waves gradually die away as they spread out, like ripples on a pond do. By measuring the height of the biggest signal on the seismogram trace, and making an adjustment for distance, it is possible to work out the magnitude.

Understanding the Earth

The mechanism of how rocks break — how long it takes for an individual fracture to happen — and the orientation of the rupture surface itself, can all be worked out from reading seismograms.

Additionally, the fine detail of the way the earthquake waves travel from the earthquake fault to any seismic recorder can be used to tell what kinds of rocks the waves have passed through along the route. As waves pass through denser rocks they are speeded up, whilst less dense rocks slow the waves down. To get a three-dimensional picture of rocks below the Earth's surface involves analysing the recordings of many earthquakes in great detail. To get a detailed picture of rocks near the surface, artificial vibrations can be generated, then collected and analysed by equipment similar to a seismic network.

2 Seismic trace marked up to show which measurements are used in determining the distance from the recording station to the epicentre, and the magnitude of the earthquake.

3 Above, laying equipment in Spitsbergen for a seismic profile to determine the depth of ice.

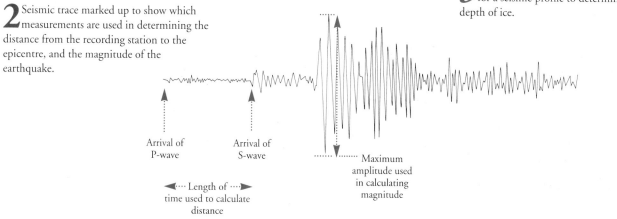

Arrival of
P-wave

Arrival of
S-wave

Maximum
amplitude used
in calculating
magnitude

◄···· Length of ····►
time used to calculate
distance

Magnitude and moment

1 Charles Richter.

Some earthquakes are noticed over only small areas, or not at all, while others are felt strongly over wide regions. Charles Richter, a seismologist in California, was the first to come up with a way of measuring earthquake sizes, and this has become known as the *Richter Scale*. Measuring magnitude poses some problems, and seismologists prefer nowadays to use another way of measuring earthquakes, based on how the rocks break; this measurement is known as the *moment* of an earthquake.

Richter Scale of magnitude

Richter devised a way of assigning numbers to earthquakes of different sizes. In this way he could be more precise in ranking the earthquakes he had measured, rather than merely calling them small, medium or large. His numbers were based on the

height of the largest amplitude on the traces recorded by his seismometers, after making a correction for the distance of the recorder from the earthquake. He called the numbers *magnitude*.

At the time, in the nineteen-thirties, Richter assigned zero to the smallest earthquake his equipment could measure. Nowadays, seismometers are much more sensitive, and can record smaller earthquakes than

Richter's zero earthquake; these are assigned negative magnitudes. On Richter's scale, the very largest earthquakes register somewhere between 8 and 9. Rocks are probably not strong enough to accumulate the amount of strain that would be needed to generate earthquakes larger than this.

2 Above, H-bomb explosion in 1952. Nuclear explosions vary in size, but typically could give out the same energy as a magnitude 5.5 earthquake.

3 Large explosions produced in quarrying could give out about the same energy as a magnitude 2.5 earthquake.

Magnitude scales

In the early days when Richter issued a press release about Californian earthquakes, he included his figure for the magnitude. The press called this the 'Richter Scale', though its official scientific title is the 'Local Magnitude Scale'. Richter only intended his method to be used for Californian earthquakes.

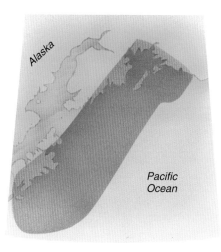

▲

The Alaskan earthquake of 1964 had a moment magnitude of 9.2. The fault plane was a thrust (at a low angle), so a very large area was affected.

4 Comparison of earthquakes of different moment magnitudes, based on the length of fault that ruptured. The three maps cover regions about the same size.

All earthquake magnitude scales are logarithmic, so that each step on the scale represents a tenfold increase in the amplitude of the ground shaking that is being measured. In terms of the energy released by the earthquake, this means a thirty-fold increase of energy for each step on the scale. Thus an earthquake of magnitude 6 releases 30 times as much energy as a magnitude 5 earthquake, and so on up the scale.

There are some problems with using the largest amplitude when the scale is applied over large distances and in different parts of the world. These have been overcome by other magnitude scales, which however, are still based on amplitudes of seismic traces.

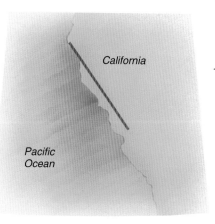

The Roermond earthquake 1992 had a ▶ moment magnitude of 5.4. The length of the fault line which slipped is so short it barely shows up on a map of this scale.

Seismic moment

Magnitudes are not very exact; readings from one type of seismometer may give different results from other types of instrument, or from other recording locations. Confusingly this may mean that one earthquake is assigned several different magnitudes, each measured by a separate instrument. A definitive magnitude can eventually be arrived at by averaging these values.

The calculation of magnitude, especially for large earthquakes, can be unsatisfactory. Instead, a measurement called moment is now being used. This is based on the area of the fault that slips in an earthquake, as well as the distance it slips. This gives a more accurate estimate of the sizes of earthquakes. The largest earthquakes have moment magnitudes between 9 and 10.

◀ The San Francisco earthquake of 1906 had a moment magnitude of 7.9 (conventional magnitude 8.3). This fault plane was near vertical and shows up as a line.

Inside the Earth

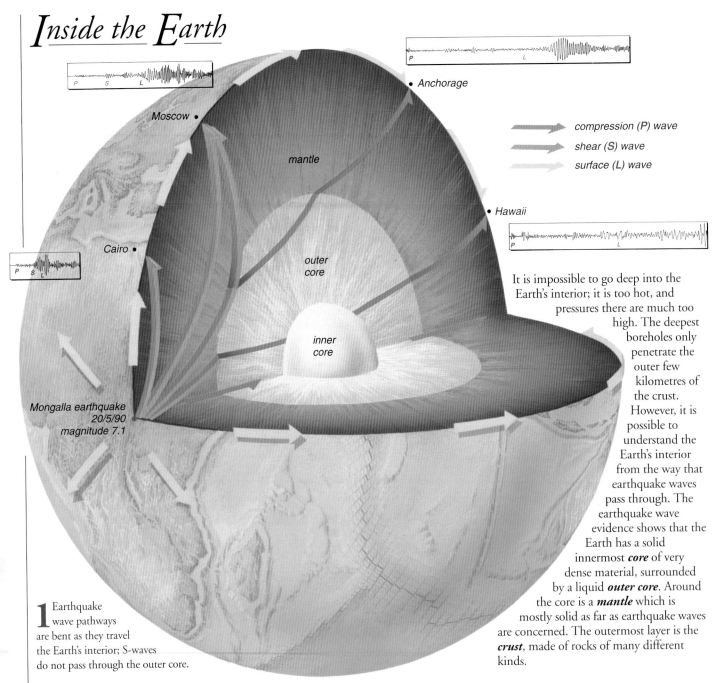

Moscow •

mantle

Anchorage •

compression (P) wave
shear (S) wave
surface (L) wave

Cairo •

• Hawaii

outer core

inner core

Mongalla earthquake
20/5/90
magnitude 7.1

It is impossible to go deep into the Earth's interior; it is too hot, and pressures there are much too high. The deepest boreholes only penetrate the outer few kilometres of the crust. However, it is possible to understand the Earth's interior from the way that earthquake waves pass through. The earthquake wave evidence shows that the Earth has a solid innermost *core* of very dense material, surrounded by a liquid *outer core*. Around the core is a *mantle* which is mostly solid as far as earthquake waves are concerned. The outermost layer is the *crust*, made of rocks of many different kinds.

1 Earthquake wave pathways are bent as they travel the Earth's interior; S-waves do not pass through the outer core.

Magnitude and moment

Density changes from P-waves

Earthquake P-waves travel through solids or through liquids, though they travel fastest through dense solids. Analysing the times of arrival of P-waves from many earthquakes shows up changes of density in the Earth's interior. On the whole, denser rocks make up deeper levels of the crust. Mantle rocks are denser overall than the crust, and they too get denser with depth. The solid and liquid parts of the core also get denser towards the centre of the Earth.

P-waves show the base of the crust as a sharp change to the more dense rocky material of the mantle. This boundary is known as the **Mohorovičić discontinuity** after its discoverer, the Croatian, Beno Mohorovičić, though normally the name of the discontinuity is shortened to **Moho**.

The Earth's soft insides

Earthquake S-waves are not transmitted through the Earth's outer core. This indicates that it is liquid. Enclosed within this liquid core lies an extremely dense solid core.

Soft or molten rock within the crust and mantle absorb S-waves. In the crust, such soft areas could be molten rock below volcanoes. Within the mantle, there lies a rather indistinct layer of soft rock, between about 100 and 200 kilometres from the Earth's surface. This layer is called the **asthenosphere**; the name means it is a region lacking in strength.

Tectonic plates

Conventionally, all the denser material above the asthenosphere is called the **lithosphere**; it is lithosphere which makes up the plates that move in plate tectonics. The whole of the thickness of the crust, together with the outermost part of the mantle go to make up the thickness of lithospheric plates.

Fine detail

The location of the core-mantle boundary is precisely shown up by earthquake waves which bounce off it, and are received as an echo at seismic recorders. Other waves which meet the core are bent (refracted) before they travel through to the far side of the globe. The amount they are bent, and the time they take to travel, tells us about the density of the material they pass through.

Supporting evidence

There is other indirect evidence to support the earthquake wave interpretation of the Earth's interior. The Earth disturbs the orbits of other planets; how much they are disturbed is an indication of the total mass of the Earth. These studies also confirm that Earth has a dense core. Study of meteorites and the chemistry of the cosmos suggest that the core of the Earth might be made of metal, probably mostly iron.

Outmoded by progress

In Jules Verne's adventure story *Journey to the Centre of the Earth*, the heroes climb into the crater of a volcano, travel through various underground passageways and come back into the light of day at another volcano on another continent. At the time he wrote this, the story probably seemed plausible to Verne's readers. Viewed with our present day knowledge about the Earth's interior, it is total fantasy.

2 As recently as 1906, William Reed published this image, showing a hollow Earth, in his *Phantoms of the Poles*.

Our restless planet

2 One hundred million years ago, Africa, India and South America had begun to move northwards from Antarctica, while the growth of the Atlantic Ocean was splitting the Americas off from the rest of Pangaea.

1 The supercontinent of Pangaea 180 million years ago, the heyday of the dinosaurs.

On the time scale of the lives of individual human beings, the continents seem to be static, and it is hard to accept that they could move. However, they do move, though very slowly. The rate of movement is only a few centimetres each year, about the rate that fingernails and hair grow.

Early ideas of Continental Drift

The suggestion that the continents move is not new. Just as soon as maps of Africa and South America were made, it was noticed that the coastlines seemed to fit each other. In the 17th century, the philosopher Francis Bacon, commented on this extraordinary match.

Early on in the 20th century, Alfred Wegener, a German meteorologist, suggested the continents might move. He used several very reasonable lines of argument to support his theory of ***continental drift***. Even so, for decades, his idea was considered to be preposterous, mostly because no one could imagine how the continents were driven through the oceans.

Evidence from the oceans

In Wegener's time, very little was known about the rocky substance that made up the ocean floor. It was only sparsely mapped and not many measurements had

been made to sound out the water depth. In the second half of the 20th century, drilling of the rocky oceanic bottom, supported by magnetic studies, accurate mapping, and detailed depth measurements, showed there was a fascinating new world below the ocean waters.

The new understanding of the rocky ocean floor overturned geological thought and speedily proved that Wegener was right. The continents move. Not only that, over hundreds of millions of years, oceans appear and disappear. The process, ***plate tectonics***, that makes and consumes oceans, is part of the process that moves continents.

Modern Plate Tectonics

It is now understood that over the last 200 million years, the Atlantic Ocean has formed, as Africa and Eurasia have drifted apart from the Americas. During the same time interval, Africa, Australia and India have moved northwards away from Antarctica, closing up an ocean which geologists call Tethys. The Mediterranean Sea, now almost a landlocked sea, is all that remains of the Tethys Ocean.

name means *all land*). Before that, there were separate continents, different in shape from those of today, which drifted towards each other to make Pangaea. Probably such drifting apart or drifting together of continents has happened a few times in the whole history of the planet; a complete cycle from super-continent to supercontinent perhaps takes 300 million years.

The movements of these huge land masses, and the making and disappearing of oceans is the *driving force that generates earthquakes*. Most earthquakes happen along the edges of the individual masses, at the borders of the tectonic plates. This is where most movement occurs. The earthquakes are the result of tearing and breaking, scrunching and crushing of rock at the edges of the plates.

5 Alfred Wegener.

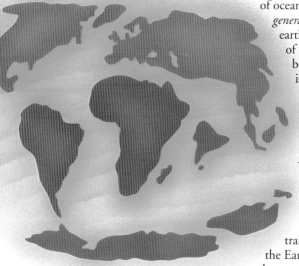

3 Sixty million years ago, India and Africa are tracking rapidly northwards, closing up the Tethys Ocean. The Atlantic Ocean continues to grow wider.

Going backwards in time, once all the continents were together in a huge supercontinent known as **Pangaea** (the

What makes plates move is not so clearly understood, but it is thought to be convection currents in the mantle. Convection transmits heat away from the Earth's white hot core. As the mantle is more or less solid, it is imagined as moving only very slowly, by a process of flow which is similar to that of glacier ice or bitumen.

4 Five million years ago, the continents were already in their present-day locations. Although India has joined onto Asia, it is still pushing northwards.

Earthquakes at plate boundaries

Most earthquakes happen at the edges of plates, where one plate meets another. Earthquakes can now be located very accurately in terms of their geographic location as well as their depth within the Earth. Once this pinpointing became possible, it was clear that some regions have earthquakes originating at depths as much as 700 kilometres, while other areas only have shallow earthquakes, none deeper than 30 kilometres. This difference between shallow and deep earthquakes marks out different kinds of boundaries between tectonic plates.

Constructive plate boundaries

At some plate boundaries all earthquakes are shallow and there are no large earthquakes. These are spreading ridge boundaries where two plates are moving apart from each other. Here, hot mantle wells up to the surface and cools and hardens to fill in any gap, tacking itself onto the edges of the plates as they spread apart. In this way new oceanic plate material is produced. One place this is happening is down the centre of the Atlantic Ocean.

Some earthquakes at spreading ridges are directly related to the rising and cooling of the molten mantle substance. Others may be from cracking in the newly-formed oceanic plate as it pulls apart, and stretches with normal faults. Few earthquakes seem to take place on the transform faults that separate individual sections of spreading ridge. Maybe these faults are lubricated by some kind of wet rock mush, so they can continuously slide without ever generating earthquakes. Most constructive boundary earthquakes take place far from land, so they rarely inflict damaging shaking to buildings.

Conservative plate boundaries

This kind of plate boundary has large and small earthquakes, which all originate at shallow depths — less than 30 kilometres. Theses earthquakes only happen in the upper part, the crust of the plate. At these plate boundaries, the substance of each plate is conserved.

One plate slides past another, and no new crust is made or destroyed. In the process, the edges of the two plates are broken into thin slivers, or crushed between a swathe of faults that snake across the landscape in a band about 100 kilometres wide. California gives an example of this type of plate boundary. Since all earthquakes at conservative plate boundaries are shallow, those quakes with the largest magnitudes cause intense shaking at the surface. Where these boundaries cross inhabited regions, damage is severe and costly.

1 **Conservative**: two plates push past each other sideways, causing earthquakes, as the edges of both plates are crushed and fractured.

2 *Constructive*: the Atlantic spreading ridge crosses Iceland in the Thingvellir National Park. Here several normal faults are more or less parallel, where Iceland is splitting apart.

3 *Constructive*: earthquakes at spreading ridges relate to hot magma rising from the mantle, and to the fractures which appear as the plates move apart.

Earthquakes at plate boundaries

volcanic island

continental
crust

oceanic
crust

descending slab

mantle

1 ***Destructive***: earthquakes are generated in the descending slab of oceanic plate. The overriding plate is also deformed, resulting in more earthquake activity.

Destructive plate boundaries

Some plate boundaries — ***subduction zones*** — are where two plates are being pushed together and an ocean plate goes underneath or subducts below another plate. As the cold oceanic slab goes down, earthquakes are generated both within it and at the interface between the two plates. Subduction zones fringe the Pacific Ocean. Here earthquakes range in magnitudes up to the largest, and in depth from shallow to deep. The large magnitude, shallow earthquakes can be highly damaging to property.

It is not possible to investigate the downgoing slab of ocean plate directly. But earthquakes tell us something about what is going on in such descending slabs. Some happen as the stiff plate is buckled or cracked as it bends downwards. Others are the result of changes brought about by the very high pressures. In these changes, individual mineral grains which make up the rock of the plate become compressed into more compact forms, and take up less space. It seems the transformation is sudden enough to generate seismic waves.

It appears that earthquakes can only originate within the crust. Marking out exactly where the deep earthquakes originate, shows up the location of the downgoing slabs of cold stiff oceanic plate.

No earthquakes originate deeper within the Earth than 700 kilometres. So at this depth, oceanic plate has apparently become totally transformed or destroyed; if it exists deeper down, oceanic plate cannot be distinguished from the rest of the mantle.

Inter-continental collisions

Over the vastness of geological time, whole oceans become subducted. This means that occasionally, when there is no longer any ocean between them, one continent meets another at a subduction zone. This is happening now in the area north of India.

The Tethys ocean north of India (pages 24–25) has vanished by subduction, bringing India into collision with Asia. In the collision, many earthquakes are generated; continental crust is less dense and cannot be subducted into the mantle.

Exceptionally high ground, including the Himalayan mountains, has been formed as the Asian plate and crumpled oceanic rocks were forced upwards over the Indian plate.

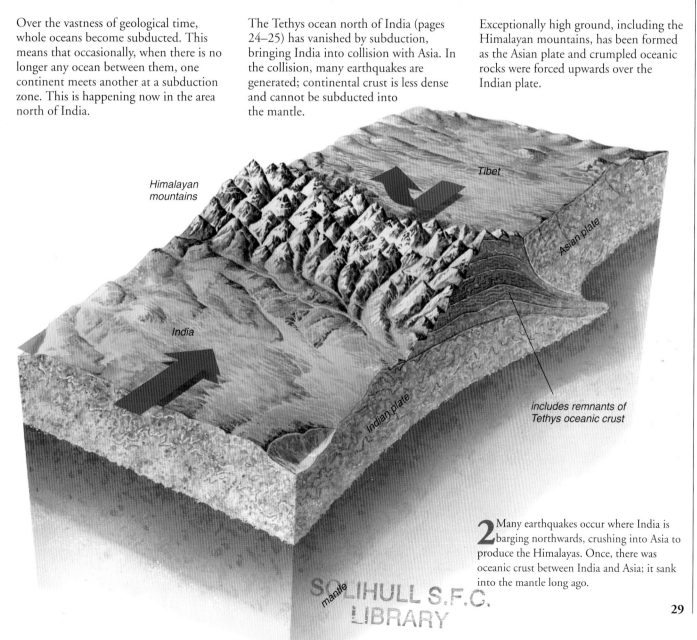

Himalayan mountains

Tibet

Asian plate

India

Indian plate

includes remnants of Tethys oceanic crust

mantle

2 Many earthquakes occur where India is barging northwards, crushing into Asia to produce the Himalayas. Once, there was oceanic crust between India and Asia; it sank into the mantle long ago.

Earthquakes within plates

A relatively small number of earthquakes happen inside the area of the plates themselves, not at plate boundaries. Most of these are within the interiors of continental areas rather than in the ocean part of plates. These *intra-plate* earthquakes may be large enough to be devastating to the lives of humans living nearby. The earthquakes occur infrequently, and it is not known if they always strike the same region within a plate.

Stresses within plates

Although the bulk of stresses caused by plate tectonic movements are released in earthquakes at plate boundaries, stresses also accumulate within the interiors of the plates. Here, old fault lines slip if they are weaker than the surrounding rock. Any such old structures might be reactivated by stresses from today's plate movements. So potentially, many old fault lines, even those far away from modern plate boundaries, could be the site of an earthquake.

Continental structure

The structure of the continents is quite complicated in many places; continents are criss-crossed by faults. Some are along old subduction zones. These are places where once there were mountain ranges which have been eroded right down to gently rolling hills, revealing folds and faults in the deep heart of the old mountain range. Other structures within continents are folds and faults where younger surface rocks have adjusted to fractures in the underlying deeper levels of the continental crust.

Like a Roman mosaic

In Roman buildings which are excavated after centuries of being buried, the mosaic floors are usually uneven, although they were level when the Romans lived there. Over the centuries since, the floor has crumpled slightly. The mosaic pieces are each still whole; all the movement has taken place along their edges. In the same way, continents fracture along old fracture lines.

Rare and costly

Fortunately intraplate earthquakes are quite rare, and tend to be smaller than plate boundary quakes. However, they usually come as a complete surprise in a place which has no history of earthquakes. If the area is densely populated, as at Latur in India where an earthquake struck in 1993, many people may be killed or made homeless. The energy of intraplate earthquakes can spread out very efficiently if it travels through old hard continental rocks. These hard rocks transmit the energy better than the younger, deformed and broken rocks of subduction zone regions. This means that larger areas experience high intensity, damaging shaking.

1 Tens of thousands of people were made homeless in the shaking that spread over India in the Latur earthquake of 1993.

Earthquakes within plates

3 Shaking was felt over a huge area in the 1811–12 New Madrid earthquakes. Shaking from the larger magnitude San Francisco earthquake of 1906, by comparison, was confined to a smaller region.

New Madrid

New Madrid on the Mississippi River in the USA had three earthquakes in 1811–1812, which were exceptionally large for intraplate earthquakes. They had magnitudes of about 8 (only three times smaller than the the San Francisco earthquake of 1906). The seismic energy from these events spread itself so efficiently through the old continental rocks that a huge area was affected, a much larger area than for the bigger San Francisco quake. The course of the Mississippi River was altered by the quakes. Fortunately the river valley was only sparsely populated at the time.

2 Contemporary engraving of the effects of the 1811–12 New Madrid earthquakes.

31

Earthquakes caused by humans

Most earthquakes are considered to be directly or indirectly caused by the plates adjusting to plate tectonic movements, but a number of small earthquakes are due to human activity. The small changes brought about by large engineering works or by mining are enough to cause earthquakes; this is known as ***induced seismicity***.

Mining

Some induced seismicity is caused by mining activity. There are three main ways in which this happens. First, the partial or total collapse of abandoned parts of mines may cause small earthquakes in the rocks above. Secondly, many coal mining areas have numerous faults criss-crossing the underground workings. Wherever the coal face comes near to a fault, the extraction causes a change in the distribution of stress within the rocks. This can induce the fault to slip, if it was almost on the point of moving anyway. Thirdly, during mining, gas which was trapped in the rocks may escape explosively as a small earthquake. Thus earthquakes, maybe up to magnitude 5, are possible as the result of underground rock or coal extraction.

In Britain the connection between coal mining and small earthquakes has been firmly established. Detailed monitoring of the earthquakes showed that most took place on working days rather than at weekends or during the

annual shut-down for the summer holidays. During the coal miners' strike of 1984–85, the earthquakes stopped almost completely. Even so, after a mine is shut down, it may be 100 years before earthquakes brought about by the mining activity cease totally.

1 Coal miners return to the surface.

2 This hole in Dudley cricket ground appeared on May 25th 1985, as a result of progressive underground collapse.

weekdays — weekend

miner's strike (Jan–Feb)   holidays (July)   coal face abandoned

3 The numbers of earthquakes in a week in a coal mining area showed a relationship to the working activity.

4 In one year, for a particular coal mine, fewest earthquakes occurred when the mine was inactive.

32

Dam building

Earthquakes are also induced by the construction of large dams. The link is easiest to spot in regions where the natural background of seismicity is low. The Kariba dam in Zambia was built in an area where no natural earthquakes had been recorded. Once the dam was built and filled, hundreds of small earthquakes were observed along the length of the reservoir. Earthquakes induced by dam construction can be as large as magnitude 6, enough to cause local damage.

High dams, especially if the water level is rapidly raised, seem most likely to induce earthquakes. The great weight from the deep water increases the load on rocks underlying the dammed valley. Earthquakes occur particularly during the period the lake is filled or emptied. Filling a dam increases the water pressure in cracks and other pore spaces within the underlying rocks. Increasing the pore-water pressure weakens the rocks, allowing earthquakes to happen more easily.

5 The Kariba dam, on the River Zambezi between Zimbabwe and Zambia, was built in an area where no natural earthquakes had been recorded. Once the dam was built and filled, hundreds of small earthquakes were observed along the length of the lake.

Oil and gas extraction

Any rapid change, increase or decrease, in the pore pressure of fluids within rocks may cause earthquakes. Natural gas and oil are fluids trapped under pressure within rocks. During extraction, the pressure of these petroleum fluids is reduced, and this may induce earthquakes. This happened at Alkmaar in the Netherlands, when natural gas extraction was followed by a number of small earthquakes that took place after 1986. Such induced earthquakes can be quite large; gas extraction in Uzbekhistan is believed to have triggered a magnitude 7 earthquake, which occurred in 1976.

Earthquakes of the world

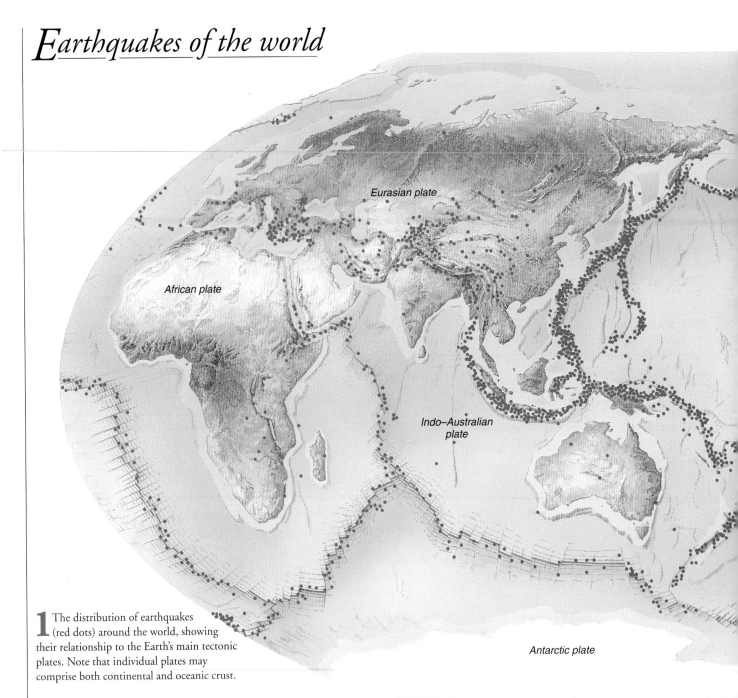

Eurasian plate

African plate

Indo–Australian plate

1 The distribution of earthquakes (red dots) around the world, showing their relationship to the Earth's main tectonic plates. Note that individual plates may comprise both continental and oceanic crust.

Antarctic plate

Earthquakes of the world

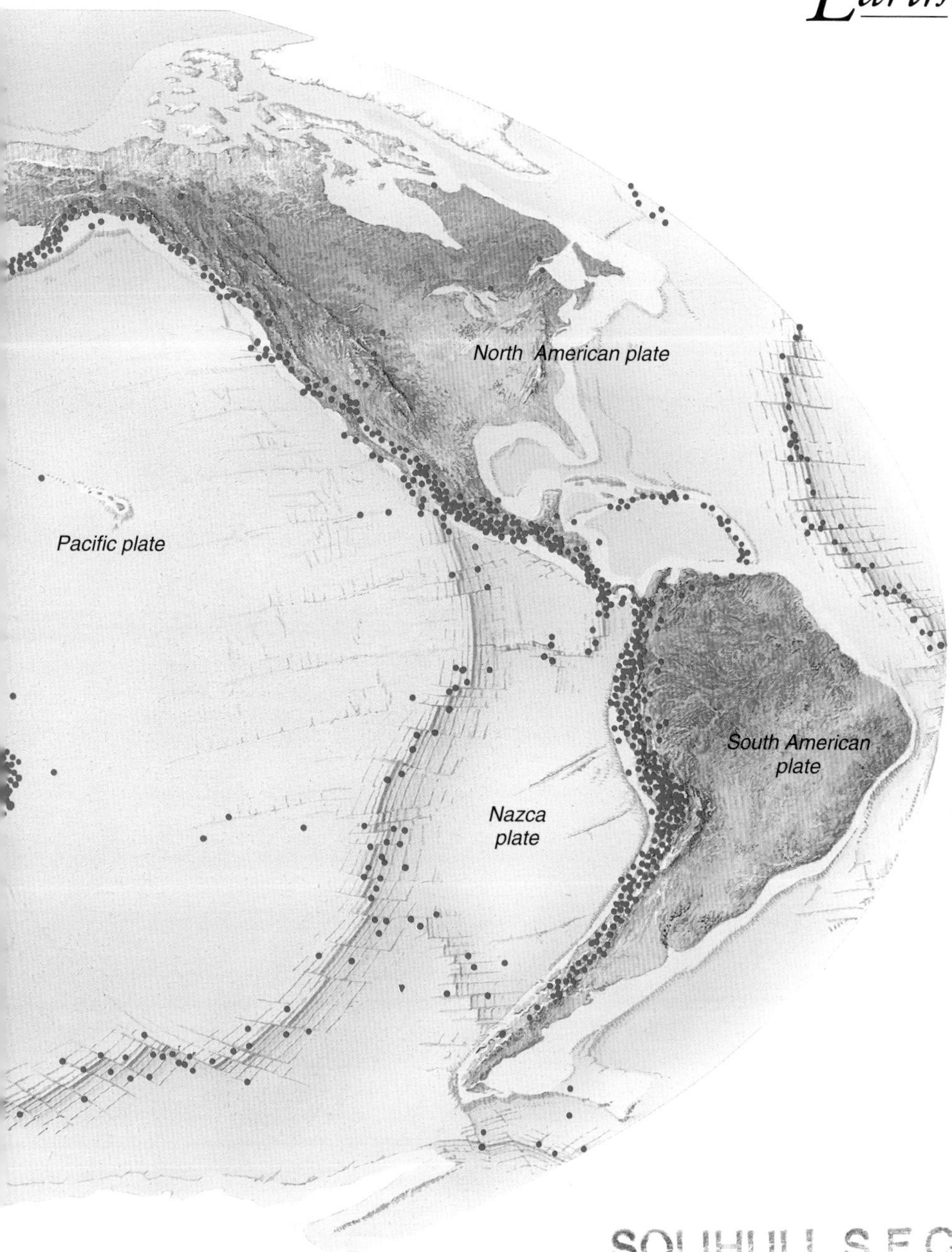

This map of earthquakes of the nineteen-eighties is similar to that for any other decade. Such maps show clearly that earthquakes happen more often in some places than in others.

The very first earthquake distribution maps, compiled in the nineteenth century showed up part of this pattern. At that time it was not possible to locate the mid-ocean earthquakes, so the database was incomplete. There was then no explanation of the pattern. Modern earthquake maps became the first piece of vital evidence that led to the development of the theory of plate tectonics. With just a few exceptions, the distribution of earthquakes defines the edges of tectonic plates.

Nowadays earthquakes can be pinpointed accurately in terms of their depth as well as their geographic location. Some are located at mantle depth, but these are within subduction zones, the origin of the individual deep earthquakes being within the subducting slab of lithosphere.

Earthquakes which are not at plate boundaries are referred to as intraplate earthquakes (page 30). There are relatively few of these and they are more scattered in distribution.

Some small earthquakes accompany the eruption of volcanoes. Also, during a volcanic eruption, there is ground tremor which relates to movements of molten rock (magma) underground. There is usually no problem in distinguishing these from the true tectonic earthquakes.

North American plate

Pacific plate

South American plate

Nazca plate

35

Earthquakes in Britain

Britain is not the place most people think of when earthquakes are mentioned, but nonetheless, earthquakes do happen. Some British earthquakes have caused damage, and shaking which was felt; they are about the size that would hardly get a mention in the more active parts of the Earth, such as the Pacific Rim.

1 Lincoln Cathedral was damaged by an earthquake in 1185.

How often? — How large?

A magnitude 4 earthquake happens in Britain about every two years. Some have caused damage to buildings, particularly in more distant historical times. Usually they were recorded because of the damage, especially that to churches and cathedrals. There are very few credible reports of earthquake deaths in Britain's historic record, and damage to buildings has never been severe.

The distribution of British earthquakes is rather irregular, and it is hard to make any sense of the pattern except over the North Sea rift. The west of England and Scotland and parts of Wales are relatively active, while north-eastern Scotland and parts of Northumberland are practically without earthquakes. The whole of Ireland is almost completely free of earthquakes.

It has been suggested that the distribution of ice sheets during the last ice maximum might be important. As the great ice sheets melted, the rocks were relieved of a huge load. It may be that the earthquakes are triggered by adjustments to this unloading.

The largest

The largest earthquake to affect the United Kingdom was centred on the Dogger Bank on 7th June 1931. With a magnitude of about 6, had it happened on the mainland, it would have inflicted conspicuous damage. As it was, it caused minor damage on the east coast of England.

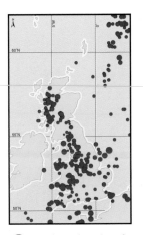

2 British earthquakes, from the 7th century onwards, are unevenly distributed.

The written record

It is possible to draw up a long catalogue of British earthquakes. It may even be quite a complete record, because Britain has had a long period during which reliable written records were kept, especially ecclesiastical records. Churches were, after all, the largest, most expensive, and structurally most daring buildings of medieval times, and were built with commitment by dedicated communities. Damage to these structures, however caused, was therefore diligently recorded, any relevant earthquakes getting a mention along the way.

On 27th April 1185, a large earthquake caused damage to Lincoln Cathedral. This seems to have been one of the strongest of medieval earthquakes in Britain.

After 1700, local newspapers began to be published in Britain, and these provide very good descriptions of local earthquake effects.

The most damaging British earthquake since Medieval times took place just south of Colchester, on 22nd April 1884.

Although the magnitude, at 4.6, was much smaller than the Dogger Bank event, damage was quite considerable in a relatively densely populated part of the country. This can be attributed largely to the shallow depth of the earthquake — about three kilometres. The soft surface rocks, of clays and gravels, also contributed to the damage. Some of the most affected buildings were already in a poor state of repair at the time. Many chimneys were thrown down, plummeting through the roofs, walls were cracked, bricks fell, and several church towers were damaged. A few people were injured, but no-one was killed.

3 Contemporary illustrations of the Colchester earthquake of 1884.

Deep and shallow earthquakes

Media reports of earthquakes invariably tell how large an event has been, but they rarely mention how deep down it originated. The depth can make a huge difference to the intensity of shaking which is experienced at the surface. It has a strong control on the area of damage, and on how much damage occurs near the epicentre.

Most earthquakes happen in the crust at a depth of less than 35 kilometres. Of these, most happen somewhere between seven and 15 kilometres, where rocks change in response to being heated to around 300– 400 degrees Celsius. At this temperature, quartz, a very common mineral within rocks, ceases to be brittle and begins to be ductile. This critical temperature is reached at different depths in different places depending on the local values of heat flow. For earthquakes to occur, that is, for rocks to fracture, they must be brittle. Where the crust is hot, the brittle-ductile transition for quartz in rocks is shallow, and so are the earthquakes. The transition imposes a lower limit on where earthquakes can occur in the crust.

It seems that the rock of the underlying mantle is too soft to fracture and generate earthquakes. However, there are some earthquakes that have deeper origins than 35 kilometres, even down as far as 600 kilometres. These occur within or up against the crustal slabs that are going down into the mantle in subduction zones. Although these are sometimes referred to as 'mantle earthquakes', they do not take place in mantle material.

Shallow earthquakes

Shallow earthquakes can cause a lot of damage relative to their magnitude; the energy of the earthquake is concentrated in a small volume of rock. A town situated immediately above a shallow quake therefore shows damage which seems out of proportion to the magnitude of the event. The San Salvador earthquake of 1986, with a magnitude of 5.3, caused considerable damage to buildings but within a small area. In all, 1000 people were killed, and 10 000 injured. The depth was only seven kilometres.

Amongst shallow earthquakes, there is some relationship between magnitude and depth, larger events tending to be deeper in origin. There is a limit on the size of very shallow earthquakes, as size is proportional to the volume of rocks involved in the faulting process. Even so, a magnitude 7 earthquake can be as shallow as five kilometres, which will cause a lot of damage in a populated area.

1 In the shallow-focus San Salvador earthquake, buildings close to the epicentre suffered severe damage.

Deep earthquakes

The deepest earthquakes originate around 680 kilometres down in the sinking oceanic crust of subduction zones. The focus is a long way from the Earth's surface, and by the time the first shock waves hit the surface, the energy is distributed over a large volume of rock. Large, deep earthquakes have huge areas of felt shaking; slight damage may occur over large areas, but the intensity of the shaking and amount of damage is disproportionately small for such large events.

The Bolivian earthquake of 9th June 1994, with a magnitude of 8.2, was a remarkable event. In spite of this large magnitude, the earthquake had little mention in the news media. With a depth of 630 kilometres, shaking was felt right into North America, as far as Toronto in Canada, some 6500 kilometres away. Moderate damage occurred in La Paz and neighbouring cities, with slight damage over a large area of South America, including the city of Brasilia.

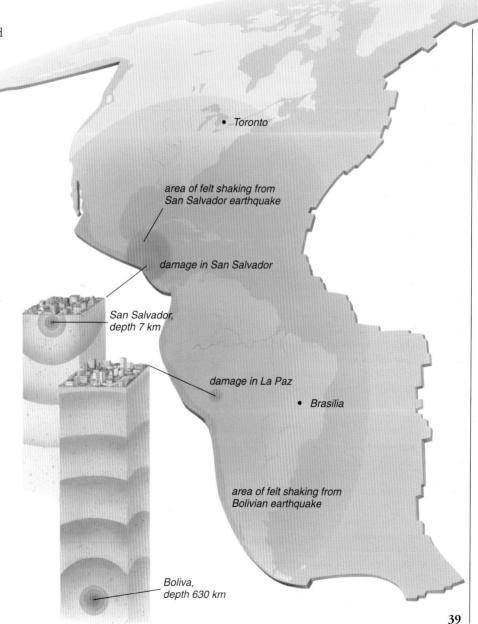

• Toronto

area of felt shaking from
San Salvador earthquake

damage in San Salvador

San Salvador,
depth 7 km

damage in La Paz

• Brasilia

area of felt shaking from
Bolivian earthquake

Boliva,
depth 630 km

2 Comparison of the shaking experienced in the deep Bolivian earthquake, magnitude 8.2 and the shallow San Salvador earthquake, magnitude 5.5.

More often than you think...

On an average day, about 45 earthquakes are recorded on the global network, but most often they are only noticed by scientists who study earthquakes. Occasionally one happens which hits the headlines in the TV news around the world; these newsworthy earthquakes are those which kill a lot of people. Without the human interest story, an earthquake is not news — too many happen every day.

Earthquakes of today

Many people believe there are more earthquakes these days than there used to be. Actually seismologists have calculated that the number of earthquakes has remained much the same, but because there are more seismometers than there used to be, more small earthquakes are recorded.

World population is increasing, so with time, ever more people are at risk of losing their lives or their homes, or both, when an earthquake strikes. Even though film and photos of human suffering resulting from an earthquake can be flashed to newspaper copy rooms and TV studios world-wide, it's strangely easy to bury such unpleasant memories. Horror stories of recent earthquakes can be kept fresh in viewers' and readers' minds for a week or two, but equally devastating earthquakes of only a decade ago are forgotten. A combination of these factors gives a false impression that there are more earthquakes now.

If by chance, as happened in 1976, several earthquakes strike in populated regions, more earthquakes are reported in the world news. The year 1976 appeared to have more earthquakes than usual to a person reading these reports. The total earthquake record for 1976 was in fact different from that of other years — it had slightly less earthquakes than is usual. However, the casualty level was very high, with over 250 000 killed by one event in Tangshan, China.

Small earthquakes happen much more often than large earthquakes. In Japan, New Zealand, Greece, California, or any other part of the world where earthquakes are most common (see page 34–35), a foreigner visiting for two weeks has a greater chance of experiencing a moderate non-damaging earthquake than a large devastating one. Even in Britain there are usually about twenty earthquakes a month, many are very small but 30, or so, are felt each year.

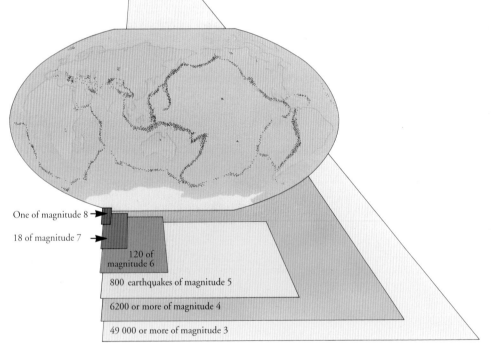

One of magnitude 8
18 of magnitude 7
120 of magnitude 6
800 earthquakes of magnitude 5
6200 or more of magnitude 4
49 000 or more of magnitude 3

1 The number of earthquakes of different magnitudes in one year.

More often than you think...

2 The tree rings of giant sequoias in the USA can be used to date earthquakes of prehistoric times. Individual trees live to be more than 3000 years old. This specimen in England is a mere 150 years old.

Evidence from the past

Along individual fault lines, similar sized earthquakes sometimes happen at regular time intervals. If there is a reliable record of past earthquakes, then the repeating pattern can be used to suggest, within a decade or so, when the next one will happen in the future.

Evidence of past earthquakes may be found in newspapers, in history books, or in ancient handwritten documents. The written historical record is very variable in length in different parts of the world. In some places such as China and Europe,

written records go back thousands of years; other places may have records which at the most are only one or two hundreds of years long.

Written records may be supplemented by evidence which is preserved in trees, or in rocks which make up the landscape. Tree rings of very old trees in California, like sequoia or bristle cones, can show decreases in the rate of growth in the years after earthquakes. This happens if their roots are disturbed or broken by ground shaking in a large earthquake, so that for a few years after, the tree grows more slowly, producing a set of unusually thin tree rings.

Earthquakes may move whole sections of landscape. In part of New Zealand, at Turakirae Head, a regular series of terraces runs round the coast; each of these is an old coastline. The sequence makes up a record of past earthquakes. During these earthquakes, the land has been raised another few metres higher above sea level each time, making a new beach. The two most recent shorelines were raised by the earthquakes of 1460, and 1855. The older terraces have probable earthquake dates of 1100 BC and 2900 BC.

3 The strand lines at Turakirae Head near Auckland, New Zealand, represent uplift of the land during four earthquakes, some of which happened in prehistoric times.

Intensity of shaking

Seismologists can determine just how severe the shaking of an earthquake has been. For the same earthquake, the *intensity* varies from place to place; usually it is greatest nearest the origin of the earthquake, dying off with distance. Intensity is worked out by observing the effects that an earthquake had at any place where shaking was noticed. These felt effects are described as the macroseismic data for the earthquake. Usually the data are reported along with a map which shows contours marking out areas of equal intensity. Intensity cannot be measured with instruments.

Interpreting intensity

The intensity is usually worked out by seismologists observing the effects on man-made objects, particularly on buildings. These effects are then compared with a standard table of intensities. This is similar to the way in which wind speeds are checked out against the Beaufort Scale. Wind speed is measured by descriptions of the effect of wind as it disturbs trees or ruffles water up into waves; earthquake intensity is measured by how much and how many buildings are damaged.

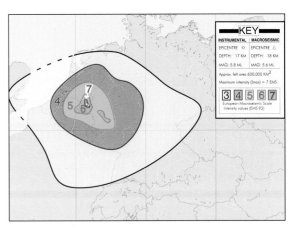

2 Isoseismal map for the Roermond earthquake of 13 April 1992. *See opposite for interpretation of intensity numbers.*

1 In the El Asnam, Algeria, earthquake of 1980, buildings constructed with their lower floors on stilts were severely damaged.

Usually, but not always, the highest intensity shaking is observed near the epicentre of the earthquake. *Isoseismals*, the lines bounding places with equal intensity of shaking, can have quite undulating shapes, as intensity correlates with landscape. Valleys which are filled with alluvial river gravels, and landfill areas show greater intensities. By contrast, regions of harder surface rock develop lesser intensities of shaking.

Easily misled

The highest intensity number, that is, the number given to the area which was most disturbed by shaking, may be reported in the popular press out of context, and without an accompanying map. This can be confusing, and very misleading, especially if the figure is wrongly stated to be the magnitude of the earthquake.

Intensity scales

Several different standard scales of intensity have been used from time to time and place to place. This is unsatisfactory for comparing intensities produced by historical earthquakes within different regions. Some scales are specific to an area, and cannot be applied elsewhere.

Documenting large events in an area which crosses many national boundaries requires close cooperation of seismologists who may have different nationalities and languages. Some intensity scales are weak because they give too little detail. There is no universally accepted standard at present, though most seismologists would ideally like to have one.

3 **A simplified Intensity Scale**
Many have twelve degrees of intensity. This one is based on the European Macroseismic Scale (EMS).

1 *Not felt.*

2 *Very weak* — felt by very few people.

3 *Weak* — felt by a few people indoors.

4 *Generally observed* — noticed by many people; windows and doors rattle. *Go to 5*

5 *Strong* — some small objects fall over.

6 *Slightly damaging* — cracks to plaster; objects fall off shelves.

7 *Damaging* — parts of chimneys fall.

8 *Very damaging* — large cracks in walls.

9 *Destructive* — some houses collapse.

10 *Very destructive* — many houses collapse.

11 *Devastating* — most buildings destroyed.

12 *Catastrophic* — everything destroyed.

Earthquake damage

Earthquake shaking in itself poses no great threat to life and limb, though it is very alarming. The effect of earthquake shaking on buildings, however, is a very serious danger to humans. This is because most buildings are not constructed to cope with such shaking; their failure is the chief cause of deaths and injuries in earthquakes. It is also the main economic cost of an earthquake.

The collapse of buildings can be very spectacular, and most news reports of earthquakes show horrifyingly mangled buildings. Most viewers probably see these images as an indication of the power of the earthquake. A truer story would also take account of any weakness or unsuitability of the buildings.

Survival of buildings

The way a building reacts to earthquake shaking depends on more than the earthquake shaking itself; the materials the building is made from, and the way in which they are put together are just as important, and often, even more important. Buildings made of heavy materials which are weakly bonded together are the most unsuitable for earthquake-prone regions. Rubble-masonry and brick buildings with low-quality mortar, and dwellings constructed of adobe mudbricks perform miserably during shaking. If such buildings also have heavy roofs, inhabitants are crushed when shaking reduces the buildings to heaps of rubble and clouds of choking dust.

Light-weight or flexible construction materials, with strong flexible connections are the best. Wooden or steel frame buildings perform well, provided the frame is properly braced. Within such buildings, the infill floor panels, walls and roofs should be tied in so they do not break away from the frame during shaking. Ideally they should be light-weight so they do not crush people if they collapse.

2 The roof and wattle-and-daub walls fell, leaving the wooden frame of the building on the left. The reinforced concrete building on the right withstood shaking better in the San Salvador earthquake of 1986, magnitude 5.3.

Many old towns and cities have elaborately-decorated masonry buildings with chimneys, parapets, cornices, pinnacles and free-standing statues. Earthquake shaking easily dislodges such building ornaments. Roof slates and tiles also fall, along with decorative cladding and glass from shattering windows. It is instinctive to rush out of buildings during an earthquake, but many people are killed or wounded by the cascade of stones, tiles and broken glass as they do so.

High-rise or low-rise buildings

Many people imagine that high-rise buildings are more dangerous in earthquakes than one or two-storey buildings. This is generally not true. The way in which tall and short buildings cope with earthquake shaking depends on the character of the shaking and on the subsoil conditions.

1 Even 170 kilometres away from the epicentre, adobe mudbrick houses were severely damaged in the 1976 Guatemala earthquake, making over ninety percent of the population homeless.

If an earthquake generates mostly high-frequency shaking, where the distance from peak to peak of the waves is small, tall buildings are hardly affected; this same kind of shaking can be devastating, though, for smaller buildings. By contrast, high-rise buildings may sway violently or fail in low-frequency shaking, where the distance between wave peaks is great. Such low-frequency shaking passes smaller buildings by.

Crushing furniture

Within high-rise buildings, low-frequency swaying may not harm the building if it is built to earthquake-resistant standards, but it can still be life-threatening for people inside. As the building flexes during shaking, it dislodges heavy furniture on upper floors. People may be crushed by filing cabinets which slide across the floor, or be buried in piles of books as bookcases topple over.

3 In the Mexico City earthquake of 1985, the vertical supports of this building failed, allowing the heavy concrete floors to collapse one on another.

4 Falling roof tiles and stucco can be a severe hazard to passers-by, or to people leaving a building during shaking. This building was damaged in the magnitude 6.9 Montenegro earthquake of 1979.

Earthquakes on record

Volcanoes usually erupt for weeks or months allowing time for photographers to get there and record the event as it continues. With earthquakes, the shaking itself takes everyone by surprise and is over within seconds or minutes. Thus, the visual record tends to be of the aftermath, of people being rescued, of fires, and collapsed buildings. It used to be only rarely that earthquake shaking was captured on film, if there happened to be a cameraman already on the scene, filming another event. Nowadays, earthquakes films are more common, at least in California and Japan, because of the large number of security video cameras which are constantly running.

Ground effects

Cracking ground

It is a popular myth that during an earthquake, great fiery chasms open up which swallow people and animals. In fact, even though rocks are fractured when earthquake shaking is generated, this does not directly result in open fissures at the ground surface. However, very strong shaking often causes soft ground to slump, and parts of embankments may slip down; these can cause local cracks in the ground. They may look alarming, but people are unlikely to be swallowed alive in them.

Horrific tales

Some early and fanciful descriptions of earthquakes depict the dead rising from their graves as the ground opened up. This exaggeration originated in lurid descriptions of the Messina earthquake in 1783, where stone tombs were disturbed by the shaking. In contemporary illustrations, bones of the dead and their coffins are depicted poking up out of the ground. Even in areas where there are no perceptible earthquakes, all cemeteries show some irregular settling of the ground. Where the ground is repeatedly dug, it is less compacted when it is refilled, and takes time to settle. Earthquake shaking causes rapid settling, allowing larger solid objects in the soil — bones and coffins — to be shaken upwards as the soil settles downwards around them.

Ground turns to liquid

Soft, wet, or sandy sediments may liquefy during earthquake shaking. Such terrain as river flood plains, level coastal flats, recently-drained lake beds and reclaimed land are particularly at risk. Earthquake shaking vibrates the sand grains, and pushes out the water. While this is happening, the soil loses all its strength and cannot support any weight — it becomes quicksand. Once shaking stops, the sand grains then compact together again.

2 A coloured contemporary engraving shows people buried up to their shoulders in liquefied ground, Port Royal, Jamaica, 1692.

1 These lakeshore houses slid closer to the lake, carried on one of several landslides which were triggered by the magnitude 7.1 Hebgen Lake, Montana, earthquake of 1959.

As ground liquefies, buildings resting on the surface sink into it, often tilting over as they sink. Usually this means they become quite unusable, and must be demolished and rebuilt even if damage is otherwise superficial. Also, buried objects including water pipes or storage tanks may float up to the surface.

It is rare in modern times for people or animals to be trapped in liquefying ground, possibly because most urbanised areas are coated with tarmac or paving stones. There are grisly reports of people being buried in liquefying ground in Port Royal, Jamaica, in the 1692 earthquake. The town was built on the tip of a sandspit, and no rock had been available locally to pave the streets. The earthquake shaking lasted five to seven minutes, time enough for people to run in panic from toppling buildings, only to sink into liquefying sand in the street. Those who were unable to free themselves whilst shaking lasted became trapped as the sand grains compacted and moulded tightly around them so they could no longer breathe.

Mudslides

Waterlogged sediments several metres below ground level may slip because they liquefy during earthquake shaking. Already loaded by the sediment layers above, they quickly fail, and the ground slides away over wide areas. In Anchorage, Alaska, in the 1964 earthquake, much of the damage was the result of failure of a waterlogged clay layer 20 metres below ground level. Whole housing districts were a total write-off after the ground subsided, houses resting precariously on higgeldy-piggeldy blocks of ground.

Build on solid rock

Houses and other structures built on soft or waterlogged ground experience much more intense shaking. The ground behaves like jelly, wobbling more and longer as the result of earthquake shaking. This amplification of the shaking greatly increases damage. In 1985, Mexico city was hit by shaking from an earthquake which originated 300 kilometres away off the Pacific coast. Houses founded on solid rock in the outer suburbs hardly shook, even birthday cards in one house were not knocked over. However, buildings on the old lake sediments in the city centre a few kilometres away were totally wrecked (page 66).

Sand fountains

Waterlogged sediments may sometimes be covered with a dry surface layer of sand or gravel or be paved. Under these circumstances, the underground watery layer liquifies, the water spurting up through the dry layer in fountains, carrying sand and silt. These fountains are observed up to several hours after earthquake shaking ends. Afterwards, piles of sand and silt, shaped like miniature volcanoes cover the ground, leading to the name *sand volcanoes* or *sand boils*.

3 Soft sediments may fail by earthquake-triggered landslipping on steep slopes, taking houses and other built structures with them, like this one in California, in 1994.

Landslides

In hilly or mountainous countryside, landslides may be triggered by earthquake shaking. Sometimes they may account for the majority of casualties from the earthquake. Usually, the landslides are from slopes that are already unstable, and the shaking is the final 'straw' that sets them off. Where valleys are blocked by landslides or avalanches, temporary dams may be created. When, inevitably, these fail, flooding downstream can be catastrophic, as in the Ecuador earthquake of 1987 when a mudflow destroyed the main oil pipeline.

Nevados de Huascarán avalanche, 1970

In 1970, an earthquake of magnitude 7.7 occurred in the Peruvian Andes. It triggered a snow and rock avalanche from the glacier-covered Huascarán mountain. Altogether 50 000 people were killed, another 50 000 were injured and half a million people were left homeless.

There had been a history of previous landslides from this mountain. An enormous landslide had occurred in the 16th century, some time before the arrival of the Spaniards. A slide smaller than the 1970 one had occurred in 1962 and had left rock steeply overhanging, so that the slope was clearly still on the point of failure.

In the 1970 event, eyewitnesses in the town of Yungay, some 15 kilometres from the mountain, heard a roaring sound as earthquake shaking died away. They spotted a dust cloud flowing down the mountain. Between 5400 and 6500 metres up the mountain, a relatively small mass of rock and ice had fallen during the 45 seconds of earthquake shaking. This triggered the collapse of the northern part of the western rock face of the peak. Within minutes, the town was engulfed; only a few, who had taken shelter by running to the top of a hill, were unharmed. The rest of the inhabitants of Yungay and the nearby Ranrahirca were buried alive.

The slide travelled fast because it fell the first 1000 metres over recent years' snow which melted and lubricated the flow. It then hit a narrow valley, which accelerated the flow as though it was coming down a ski jump. The flow launched into the air, overtopped a hill, and divided into two, one part taking the Yungay valley, the other making its way towards Ranrahirca.

The flow travelled at 280 kilometres an hour, throwing boulders out at the front of the flow. The boulders reached an amazing 1000 kilometres an hour, as they were flung four kilometres through the air. Abrasive mud, driven by a powerful wind, was spattered sideways out of the avalanche as it fell. This stripped leaves from trees, and was powerful enough to shed bare skin.

The devastating flow banked around the sides of the river valleys as it fell, like a racing car on a banked circuit. Most of the mud and boulders came to rest in a ten-metre thick blanket on the flat valley floor around Yungay and Ranrahirca, but some flowed on down the Rio Santa valley to the sea as a mudflow. In the future, Nevados de Huascarán will quite possibly release more landslides in response to other earthquakes.

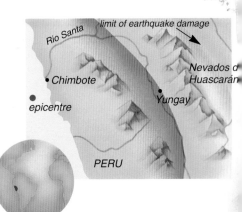

1 Location of the epicentre and area of the 1970 earthquake which triggered the Nevados de Huascarán avalanche.

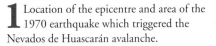

48

Nevados de
Huascarán
(6768 m)

2 Artist's impression of the Nevados de
Huascarán avalanche.

Yungay

Ranrahirca

Mancos

Tsunamis

When a large earthquake occurs under the sea, not only are shock waves transmitted through the rocks and noticed as shaking, but the impact also affects the ocean water. A sequence of water waves spreads out from the earthquake epicentre, and may travel over an entire ocean. As these waves break on distant shores, thousands of kilometres from the original quake, they can travel inshore well above high water mark. The water rushes inland with great force, causing considerable damage. It may uproot trees, and pick up ships which were at harbour, carrying them inland and smashing them against buildings.

Pacific Ocean

Tsunami waves are most common in the Pacific Ocean, where all shores are earthquake-prone; the name *tsunami* is a

1 Artist's impression of a tsunami wave striking a Japanese coastline.

Japanese word. Such sea waves are less common in the Atlantic Ocean, where shorelines have few earthquakes. The tsunami following the Lisbon earthquake (page 3) is a rare example.

On a shore well beyond the area where shaking is felt, the first warning of a tsunami may be that the sea is sucked away from the shore, as though the tide has gone right out, but within just a few minutes. Only minutes later, the water returns with a huge breaking wave, engulfing not only the area just recently dry, but also running inshore. Commonly the first wave is followed at intervals of fifteen to twenty minutes by more waves, some of which may be even larger than the first.

Fish may be stranded on the foreshore as the water level falls. People who live near the shore are sometimes tempted to gather this unusual bonus of free food, only to be drowned by the returning wave as they do so. Others may be drowned as they watch the waves from what they thought was a safe position, unaware that the later waves could be higher, or imagining that the second or third wave was the last.

Measuring tsunamis

There are two different ways of measuring tsunamis. Run-up height is the maximum altitude above sea level reached by the incoming water.

2 Parts of the Pacific coastline of Japan are protected by giant concrete hexapods and a concrete wall to prevent erosion by tsunami and typhoon waves.

This is often as much as 30 metres for a strong tsunami. The other is the wave amplitude, the actual height of the wave from crest to trough. Usually this is only about two metres but can go up to ten metres in extreme cases. News reports often only mention the run-up height, which can give the impression that 30 metre-high waves were seen, when in reality they were much smaller.

Tsunami international warning system

Throughout the Pacific region, a tsunami warning system exists. Not every earthquake around the Pacific Rim causes tsunami waves, so warnings are only issued following an earthquake once water waves are reported in the epicentral region. Provided local damage is not so intense as to prevent the message getting out, the news of the impending wave is flashed to receiving stations across the Pacific Ocean. Local populations can then be warned to keep away from likely danger areas.

3 An enornmous earthquake in Chile may have initiated a landslide which produced the tsunami.

Chilean tsunami

In 1960, a magnitude 8.5 earthquake in Chile caused tsunami waves across the Pacific Ocean. Fifteen minutes after shaking ended, the first water waves hit the coasts locally, drowning thousands of people.

Fifteen hours later, the water waves arrived at the Hawaiian islands. Warnings had been broadcast since early evening, and many people had gone to the beaches to watch. As a result, 61 people died and 282 were injured in Hawaii.

Twenty two hours after the earthquake, the tsunami reached Japan, 17 000 kilometres away. In the night darkness, waves four to six metres high destroyed 5000 homes and killed 180–190 people.

6 At the coast, tsunami waves smash buildings and uproot trees, and toss small boats as if they were toys and carry them inland.

7 In shallow water, the waves slow down and break. Water is sucked back in front of each great breaker. As wavelength decreases, the height of the wave increases.

Japan

• *Hawaii*

Pacific Ocean

Chile

4 In deep ocean water, tsunamis travel at about 700 kilometres an hour. In the deep ocean water, the waves are so small they are unnoticeable.

5 In shallower water, they are slowed to about 100 kilometres an hour. The water piles up, forming big breaking waves. The red line shows the increasing height of the water wave.

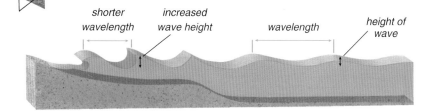

shorter wavelength

increased wave height

wavelength

height of wave

Death tolls and casualties

Earthquakes that get reported in the media are those which kill many people. Most earthquake fatalities are people who are trapped in buildings which collapse; buildings, not earthquakes, are the killer. The most dangerous earthquakes are those that happen at times when people are indoors, in places where buildings are weak and cannot withstand shaking.

Population density

Earthquakes are unevenly distributed around the world; the great majority occur around the Pacific Rim. It happens that parts of these regions are also some of the most densely populated parts of the world. Earthquakes that hit such regions take the greatest toll of lives.

Even the very largest earthquakes can have little or no effect on human activity if the region is sparsely populated. The great magnitude 8.2 earthquake of 23rd May 1989 in the Southern Ocean was just noticeable in the nearest land, parts of New Zealand, and it went practically unreported in news bulletins.

Kinds of building

In societies where stone or adobe mudbrick is the principal building material, death tolls are largest if an earthquake occurs when most people are indoors. These traditional homes have

advantages; they are made of locally available material, they are cool in the heat of day and hold heat through cold weather. But such heavy, inflexible buildings cannot withstand earthquake shaking; they collapse, crushing people inside. However, where dwellings are built of wood, or felt and other cloth, even a night-time earthquake will cause few deaths.

1 Peru: if an earthquake occurs at night, in a region of adobe mudbrick homes, death tolls can be very high.

In industrialised western societies, night-time earthquakes cause fewer deaths, because homes tend to be suitably built to withstand earthquakes. In the 1994 Northridge, California, earthquake, very few died, partly because the quake happened in the early hours of a public holiday, when folk were still in their homes. The other factor was the strong but flexible timber-framed houses, which did not collapse on their inhabitants.

Time of day

In non-industrialised societies, where agriculture is the main occupation, most people are likely to be outdoors during the daytime. Earthquakes which happen during the day cause few deaths in such communities. It has been estimated that if a great earthquake such as the one which hit the rural community around Kangra in India in 1905 should recur today, 88 000 might be killed if it happened during the day. If it happened in the morning or evening, the likely death toll would be 177 000, but if it were to strike at night, the dead might number 344 000.

Industrialised societies are most vulnerable to earthquakes which occur during travelling time to and from work, where crowded railtracks, bridges and motorways may fail during shaking. If the Northridge earthquake had happened on a working day during the rush hour when many people were on the freeways which collapsed, the death toll would have been much higher.

Death tolls and casualties

The earthquake of 23rd January 1556, in Shanxxi province, China is estimated to have killed 830 000 people. Many people in Shanxxi lived in cave houses excavated in loess; these are cool in summer, warm in winter, easily enlarged to make space for expanding families, whilst the local landscape provides the materials. But the fragile calcite cement which holds together the wind-blown grains of loess failed during earthquake shaking, burying the hundreds of thousands of people as they slept.

In China in 1976, the Tangshan earthquake killed about 255 000 people. Most died in their sleep, as the earthquake struck at 3.43 am, when their brick homes collapsed on them. China is among the most densely populated regions of the Earth, so it is not surprising that the historically highest death tolls are to be found there.

2 Mexico City: damage to commercial buildings causes highest death tolls if an earthquake occurs during working hours.

Highest death tolls

A figure of 1 000 000 deaths is sometimes quoted for the earthquake of the 20th May 1202 in the Lebanon. This is certainly a gross overestimate, but the toll was very high.

3 Kobe: failure of transport networks causes highest casualties and deaths if an earthquake occurs during the rush hour.

Earthquake prediction

As global population has risen, so the desire to try to save lives by predicting or preventing natural disasters has become more urgent. Earthquakes cannot be prevented, and at present they cannot be meaningfully or reliably predicted. To be useful, a prediction must state the size, the place and the timing of an impending earthquake. It is no use to know that there will be a big earthquake tomorrow, without knowing precisely where it will happen.

General forecasts of earthquakes are possible. Places where large earthquakes may be expected in the near future can be outlined. Usually these are zones a few hundred kilometres across, where there has been little seismic activity in recent years, flanked on either side by zones of many earthquakes. These seismic gaps are areas where stress is not being released, so a big event could happen soon; the longer the time wait, the larger the event is likely to be.

Foreshocks

A great earthquake may be preceded by a distinctive pattern of smaller events, after a long period of quiet. These are called foreshocks. Provided they are recognised as foreshocks, a warning can be issued. While some earthquakes are preceded by foreshocks, not all are. And most small earthquakes are simply independent events, not followed by related earthquakes.

Geophysics

In the period preceding an earthquake, when stress is building up in the region where rock will eventually fracture, physical properties change within the rocks which are under stress. These changes may be measurable. The types of physical property being investigated include electrical resistivity, and the speed at which vibrations (such as shock waves from quarry blasts) are transmitted through the stressed rocks.

Suggestions have been made that stressed rocks give off electromagnetic discharges before an earthquake happens. These could be related to the weird lightning effects which are sometimes seen during large earthquakes, known as 'earthquake lights'. Attempts are being made to measure these discharges, but results are inconclusive so far.

Radon gas

Radon gas is emitted continuously from rocks and soil, though levels vary widely from place to place. It is thought that the rates of radon emission increase in the weeks and days preceding an earthquake. This could happen as tiny cracks develop in stressed rock, increasing the surface area and allowing radon gas to escape faster than usual.

Animals behaving oddly

Classical Roman literature writes of coralled horses panicking and wild animals coming down into inhabited valleys just before earthquakes. It is as though animals can sense danger in a way which humans probably cannot. Japanese literature also refers widely to animals reacting before earthquakes, the older references even suggesting mythical animals might cause the earthquakes. In modern times, a successful prediction of a 1975 earthquake in China used, among other things, the peculiar behaviour of animals; there were reports of snakes and other hibernating animals crawling from their holes in mid-winter in the days and hours before the quake.

1 Cockroaches are highly sensitive and could detect elusive earthquake precursors.

2 Parkfield: the lid to the left is over a strainmeter which measures strain in the rocks 200 metres down, while the solar panels at the surface transmit data back to the laboratory.

What next?

Prediction of an earthquake in an urban area could lead to panic and confusion, as citizens try to leave the built-up areas. People travelling are in danger during an earthquake; trains may be derailed, bridges and freeways might collapse, landslides could cut roadways, The overall result could be that more lives are lost than would have been lost if all had stayed at home.

Predictions, to be socially acceptable, must be right every time. A false prediction, one which was not followed by a quake, could cause almost as much economic loss as the occurrence of an unpredicted earthquake. Loss to businesses which shut down temporarily, the cost of transport and temporary accommodation, and loss of tourism could be severe.

Some scientists are coming to the conclusion that earthquakes are by their very nature unpredictable. Possibly, large earthquakes start out as small ones in the first few seconds as the rock starts to break. What started out as a small earthquake could then grow into a larger earthquake in a kind of cascade effect, as more and more stressed rock is triggered into joining the rupture. If this theory is correct, there is no possibility of predicting the small earthquake that starts the cascade. It would just be too small to give off any distinctive warning signals, and would be indistinguishable in advance as a triggering event rather than any other small earthquake.

3 Parkfield: creepmeters installed in the ground can detect minute movements, as small as 0.02 mm, which might be precursors to an earthquake.

Predicting earthquakes at Parkfield

So far it has proved impossible to find a set of precursor events which reliably indicate that an earthquake is about to happen. But if such precursors really do exist, Parkfield, California, looks like a good place to find them.

Parkfield is a small village on the San Andreas fault, about 280 kilometres south east of San Francisco. It has experienced earthquakes of magnitude 6 on a regular basis, roughly one every 22 years. On the basis of this regular repeating pattern, the United States Geological Survey predicted in 1984 that the next magnitude 6 earthquake would occur in 1988. They estimated a margin of error of five years either way.

Looking for earthquake precursors

To try to find the events that might precede an earthquake means using many different types of measuring equipment in a likely region, like Parkfield. On the expectation that the precursors would be hard to spot, many sensitive instruments, capable of detecting even the smallest changes, have been used at Parkfield. All changes, even quite unlikely ones, are considered. The name of the village of Parkfield is now well-known among seismologists, as one of the most wired-up natural earthquake laboratories — it's just waiting for an earthquake to happen.

2 The small settlement of Parkfield is well-known to seismologists around the world.

There is a very dense array of computer-linked seismometers, some mounted at the surface, others located in boreholes. These give a reliable three-dimensional interpretation of even the smallest earthquakes, and can assess which of them might turn out to be foreshocks. One borehole alone has 116 seismometers at different depths.

Thirteen creepmeters are in place to measure any movement which might be happening along a fault plane prior to an earthquake. Strainmeters are placed to detect whether the rocks are being deformed, stretched or squeezed near the fault itself.

1 A laser system is being used to monitor movements on the San Andreas fault at Parkfield, California.

Predicting earthquakes at Parkfield

Tiltmeters show any tilting of the ground which might be caused by localised swelling of underground rocks. Networks of laser-ranging equipment are used to detect any large scale changes in ground levels.

Changes in levels of gases, especially radon and hydrogen gases, might also be indicators of an impending earthquake; these are monitored. Magnetometers are placed to show any changes in rock magnetism, while radio frequency monitors search for electromagnetic emissions which might precede an earthquake. Local changes in the Earth's resistivity are measured with telluric current monitoring devices.

1988 came and went. In 1992, a magnitude 4.7 event was announced to be a foreshock to the expected magnitude 6 event. No magnitude 6 earthquake followed. 1993, the latest time given on this prediction passed, but still no magnitude 6 earthquake occurred.

A recalculation of the statistics of the historic pattern of earthquakes showed a flaw in the original analysis, and a new prediction was announced for an earthquake in 1999, with a margin of error of one year. With the measuring network installed, the painstaking search for the elusive precursors continues.

3 The anchor end of a creepmeter, installed underground at Parkfield, to detect any ground movement which might herald a future earthquake.

*H*azard estimation

Although earthquakes cannot be prevented or reliably predicted at present, there is an alternative strategy for reducing their disaster potential. This is to take defensive measures in advance of an earthquake occurring. If a community is prepared for an earthquake, predicting it in advance is not important — people will be able to ride out the shockwaves.

There are three elements in preparing for earthquakes. The first is to assess the severity of the hazard — how frequent are earthquakes? The second is to construct buildings that have the right amount of strength. And the third is to educate people how best to survive an earthquake.

Lifetimes of buildings

An ideal way to avoid loss of life and property would be to design and build all structures in earthquake-prone regions to be unaffected by earthquake shaking. This would be impossibly expensive; the more earthquake-proof the building, the more it costs. In practice, a compromise is usually made, weighing up the increased cost of construction against the likelihood of damage by earthquake shaking. This is done partly by taking into account how long the building is expected to last.

Many modern structures are designed and built to have a specific lifetime — this could be 50 years for a bridge or a section of motorway, or a factory. To make a building safe for its lifetime, the designer might ask a seismologist to calculate the expected chances of different amounts of earthquake shaking in this period. This will give him an idea of how much strengthening to include to make the building acceptably safe.

Patterns of earthquakes

For a particular region, a seismologist can work out how often earthquakes of different magnitudes have happened by analysing the historic record of earthquakes. It is also possible to show where they occur with respect to the construction site — are they close by or far away? Since the strength of shaking decreases with distance from the epicentre, this is an important factor in calculating the probability of severe shaking at the site of the new building.

1 Buildings, such as St Vitus Cathedral, Prague, decorated with pinnacles and towers, are only suitable in regions where earthquakes are small and infrequent.

2 This building in Guatemala City may have survived many earthquakes, but is now seriously damaged around the window.

Safe as houses?

A series of probabilities can be calculated — for example, there might be a one in three chance of an earthquake causing shaking of intensity 6 or greater at the site over the next 50 years.

For intensity 7 or greater, it might be a one in ten chance, and for intensity 8 or greater, a one in a hundred chance. With this probability, the designer has a choice: designing the building to withstand shaking of intensity 6 will make it 90% safe over its lifetime. To make it 99% secure, it must be designed for intensity 7, and so on.

3 The supporting columns in Grecian temples were anchored with soft lead metal ties to help them withstand earthquakes.

4 This nuclear power station is certified as complying with stringent earthquake-resistant design regulations.

Each step which increases the earthquake-proofing of a building can greatly increase its cost. The designer's decision on how safe is 'safe enough' would be influenced not just by the amount of money the client will pay, but also by the type of building, and the consequences of it being damaged. A jam factory would not require such stringent earthquake-proofing as a nuclear power station.

Usually the earthquake-resistant design ensures the building will not collapse on its occupants rather than trying to prevent damage completely.

In many countries there is legislation which obliges building owners to have certain minimum standards of earthquake safety. Such legislation controls the designer's decisions on the level of safety features to be included.

Earthquake engineering

Most deaths in earthquakes are caused by collapsing buildings and other man-made structures. People spend most of their time in buildings; at home, in offices and factories, in hospitals, religious buildings, railway stations, shopping precincts, and so on. All these buildings, if they are built to earthquake-resistant standards, reduce the disaster potential of earthquakes.

The builder and designer can make great contributions to reducing the impact of earthquakes on humans. As long as buildings do not collapse, not many people will be killed when an earthquake occurs. It is impossible to build buildings that will not be damaged at all.

Building homes

Wooden frame buildings have the advantage of flexibility; they bend with shaking, and are less likely to collapse as long as they are in good condition. The drawback is that they are more susceptible to fire. Some regions which are prone to earthquakes do not have enough wood for building. Heavy masonry is used for building in many parts of the world. The quality of mortar has a significant effect; the stronger the mortar, the stronger the building will be. A simple and cheap method of reinforcing traditional masonry or brick houses is a steel cable just below roof level. This simple device can be very effective in holding a house together, and can greatly reduce the number of casualties in an earthquake.

Tower blocks

Blocks of flats, offices and warehouses should have adequate lower floors, which generally should be stronger and heavier than higher storeys. Large open spaces for ground floor parking are weaknesses which may bring down an entire building, even though the rest was adequately built. Hotels often have large reception lobbies, lounges and dining rooms. These large unsupported spaces increase the vulnerability of the building.

Irregular-shaped buildings, or those with lift shafts or stairways added at the side are more dangerous than symmetrical buildings. The different parts of the building vibrate at different rates, for example, causing increased damage at the joins. Tall buildings built close together may pound against one another as they separately sway in an earthquake.

Earthquake resistance

Buildings are naturally constructed to take vertical strain, as they have to bear their own weight. Often, they are not adequately designed to cope with lateral forces such as the sideways shaking they experience in earthquakes. Yet in earthquakes, sideways shaking is usually much more severe than vertical shaking, so adding lateral strengthening to buildings can help them withstand

1 In downtown San Francisco, the modern pyramid building is designed to earthquake-resistant standards.

earthquakes. In countries which regularly experience stormy weather, buildings are given lateral strengthening against high winds; this gives them earthquake resistance as well.

Some buildings are earthquake-proofed by isolating them from the shaking ground. Rubber or steel pads may be placed between the building and the ground below, to help reduce the amount of shaking which transmits into the structure. Other buildings are made resistant by reinforcing their concrete structure with extra steel at certain critical points. Shaking is then absorbed as the steel bends and buckles, but the building does not collapse.

Unfortunately, earthquake-resistant building design can be dull to look at. Squat, square buildings with no architectural ornament look boring and are unattractive to live with. There often has to be a compromise between providing something which is attractive to look at and to live in on a day-to-day basis, and providing safety in an earthquake which may or may not happen within a lifetime.

Building codes

It is possible to draw up guidelines which assist in designing buildings to resist earthquake shaking reasonably well. It is not always as easy to enforce such building codes. Each earthquake which has involved great loss of buildings has

revealed inadequacies of design, poor materials or workmanship, as well as direct flouting of existing codes of building practice. The 1985 Mexico City earthquake revealed that despite the experience of a previous quake, unsuitable buildings had again been sited on the less adequate ground.

2 The beehive-shaped building in Wellington, New Zealand, is designed to modern earthquake-resistant standards.

3 Simple illustrations can be used to get the message across, such as apppropiate building and construction methods.

Planning for earthquakes

Whilst engineers and designers have a role to play in minimising earthquake casualties, politicians and planners can also help to reduce the disaster level. This planning is especially important in built-up areas with dense population, but it can be significant in rural communities too. Planning can make sure that even in the event of a damaging earthquake, there is a clear line of action to deal with the immediate emergency. It should include plans which go beyond the emergency stage into the period of restoration and recovery.

2 A row of street telephones to enable the homeless in Kobe to contact friends, relatives and business associates during the chaos after the 1995 earthquake.

1 Child survivor of 1995 earthquake on Sakhalin Island, Russia, which killed more than 550 people.

Disaster plan: emergency

This entails a plan of action to deal with the immediate aftermath of shaking. There should be clearly understood chains of command for decision making, for assessing what emergency supplies are needed, controlling fires, providing access to areas most affected which might be cut off by fallen buildings or landslides, providing medical support, checking for toxic or hazardous leaks from industrial sites, issuing emergency public information, and for managing volunteer help.

3 Fighting fires at Berkeley California, in the immediate aftermath of the 1989 earthquake.

4 Following the Kobe earthquake in 1995, fires were extensive in Kobe City, and whole housing districts went up in flames which were fanned by strong winds.

Planning for earthquakes

Disaster plan: restoration

This phase begins immediately the earthquake strikes and lasts for a few weeks. Much of this planning must be done on the spot, at the time, and only generalised advance planning is possible.

Planning for restoration means ensuring that through all the chaos, there is access to earth-moving equipment and tracker dogs to find those injured and dead who are buried under collapsed buildings. It means reassuring the population through the frightening period when aftershocks occur. It is about arranging for buildings to be inspected to determine which are safe, and which should be demolished. It involves restoration of clean water and power supplies as well as managing money and help from outside disaster agencies.

The period of time immediately after shaking has ended, and before clearing up begins, is an important time for earthquake engineers. Their observations of damaged structures can be used to assess the severity of the shaking, and draw up isoseismal maps. They also show how existing buildings have responded to shaking, giving the clearest indication as to how earthquake-resistant buildings of the future might be better designed and built.

1 Above, emergency services at work in the Marina district of San Francisco on October 18th 1989, following the magnitude 6.9 Loma Prieta earthquake. The timber-framed buildings shifted off their foundations.

2 Left, washing clothes in the ruined streets of Mexico City, following the 1985 earthquake.

3 Right, rescue workers and homeless people were fed from makeshift kitchens in the days following the Kobe earthquake.

Planning for earthquakes

4 Above, specially-trained tracker dogs were used night and day to help locate people trapped in the buildings which fell in the Armenian earthquake of 1988.

Planning for earthquakes

Disaster plan: recovery

This phase could last a year or more. It deals with returning life to normal, disposing permanently of the debris from collapsed buildings, rebuilding houses, roads and other structures, and putting the local economy — shops, offices and factories — back into action. Looking further towards the future, before rebuilding begins, the damage should be assessed to determine which areas were most affected. If a microzonation map exists, it should be checked and updated for hazardous ground.

Zoning the hazard

Once the vulnerability of a planning region is known, planners can have maps made to show variations within their area. Such microzonation maps might show where buildings are situated on soft or reclaimed land. These would be especially prone to intense shaking, or to liquefaction. Waterfront areas may be marked if they are susceptible to tsunami waves. Steep slopes which may be at risk from landslides should be identified. Potential landslides which threaten communication links such as railway lines and roads, or electricity power lines should also be noted. Water and gas pipes which cross fault lines, and could be fractured during an earthquake, are a major risk.

1 Clearing the rubble of collapsed buildings helps to maintain roadways through the devastated town of Neftegorsk, Russia, following the earthquake of 1995.

2 A simple microzonation map of Mexico City outlines areas of ground of variable hazard. In the 1985 earthquake, severe damage occurred over the Lake Bed Zone.

Once the microzonation maps are drawn up, emergency facilities should be located well away from any hazardous areas which have been identified. Hospitals and fire stations should be sited in relatively safe areas, so they continue to function through the emergency period.

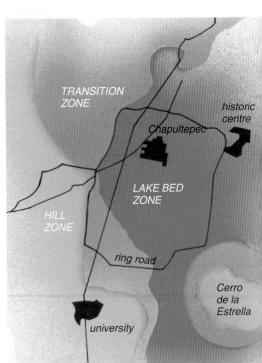

LIMITED ENTRY

OFF LIMITS TO UNAUTHORIZED PERSONNEL

Authorized by Governing Authority.

Warning:
This structure has been damaged and its safety is questionable. Enter only at own risk. Aftershocks or other events may result in death or injury.

Date _Oct. 21/89_
Time _4:00 PM_

This facility was inspected under emergency conditions for:
_S.F.B.B1_
(Jurisdiction)
on the date and time noted.

Restrictions on use:
☐ Entry for emergency purposes only
☑ Other
CAN REMOVE CONTENTS

Facility Name and Address:
244 FRONT STREET

Inspector ID/Agency:
_1036 & 1037_

Do Not Remove this Placard until

3 Above, the El Asnam, Algeria, earthquake of 1980 dislocated roads and railways, which were rapidly reinstated.

4 Left, buildings which are unsafe should not be entered; aftershocks, which may persist over weeks or even months, could cause sudden collapse.

5 Chile: churches and other important buildings are repaired, wherever possible.

67

Insurance against earthquakes

1 The Getty Museum at Malibu, California, has taken elaborate precautions to minimise damage to works of art during an earthquake, by anchoring statues and other heavy items.

As the world's population increases, so more and more people are exposed to the risk of earthquakes.

Many of the regions which are the most densely populated are also regions which have large and damaging earthquakes. In terms of financial loss, cities are particularly at risk. Here, not only do many people live, but also there are specialised buildings with expensive contents, and the risk is concentrated in a small area which could be totally devastated.

The cumulative effect of a large number of claims from an urban area can be enormous, and seems to increase as time goes by. The Northridge earthquake of 1994 was the most expensive natural disaster in the whole history of the USA, with a cost of $13 billion. Yet this was not a particularly great earthquake; its magnitude was only 6.8. It was far from being the 'Big One', a magnitude 8 on the San Andreas Fault, that Californians dread.

Insurance claims from the 1906 San Francisco earthquake were largely covered by Lloyds, whose international reputation grew from their ability to survive this catastrophe. Insurance claims from a similar earthquake today could prove to be beyond the resources of the insurance companies involved. Some companies are aware of their commitment and impose indemnity limits, to keep down the size of individual claims. Others specifically exclude earthquake losses altogether. In Japan, earthquake insurance is so uneconomic for the policy holder, who may recover only a small proportion of the cost of the damage from the insurer, that many buildings are uninsured against earthquakes.

An insurable risk?

The way insurance works is that a large number of people pay premiums to provide the funds to pay out to the few who claim. Usually all the participants in the scheme are equally exposed to risk. The kind of events covered are expected to be uncommon, and to strike by chance. Earthquakes do not fit well with this model for a variety of reasons.

Some individual insurance companies concentrate their business in small geographic areas. Following an earthquake, a large proportion of their customers may each make a claim for the damage caused, exceeding the pool of funds held as cover. Additionally, the vulnerability of insurance companies may not have been fully appreciated in advance.

There are knock-on consequences of an earthquake which may not have been taken into account. These include loss of goods and machinery which are damaged when the building which housed them collapsed.

There may be claims for damage that takes place during salvage. Businesses which are heavily computerised may claim for loss of information stored in the computers. People whose useful working life is brought to an end by injuries resulting from the earthquake may also make claims. There may be loss of incomparable art objects in museums and libraries, and damage to historic buildings.

Claims could include not just reinstatement of buildings and contents, but also loss of business during the aftermath and rebuilding phase.

A community may suffer a general and widespread loss of economic production. For example, hotels commonly have large open lobbies and showy design which make them especially vulnerable to earthquake shaking. In a region which depends heavily on tourism, the local economy may be paralysed until hotels can be rebuilt. The overall loss to the community would include failure of many businesses which depend on tourism.

Earthquakes strike again and again in some regions, with a regularity that can be predicted in a very general sense. In other areas, regions where only small earthquakes happen, or away from plate boundaries, there is no apparent regularity, and earthquakes seem to be truly the chance events that are a normal insurable risk. The exposure to risk of earthquakes is therefore not equally spread; it is questionable whether communities in areas of low seismic risk should subsidise the insurance premiums of those in known higher risk areas.

Financial planning to cope with the consequences of the most destructive earthquakes may nowadays be beyond the means of individuals, businesses and insurance companies, and even of some governments.

2 The insurance claims from the devastated Kobe City included buildings and their contents, as well as business losses.

3 The contents of buildings increase the total insurance losses in an earthquake.

69

Prepare to survive

The most cost-effective way to reduce earthquake casualties is to improve public awareness of what to do when an earthquake strikes. This way, each person can help to save his own life and those of others. Many countries now have earthquake education programmes, with advertising campaigns to increase awareness.

Before an earthquake

People who live in earthquake-prone regions can make advance preparations. Keeping emergency supplies is a good idea. Tinned food, tin opener and bottled water are essentials. A working torch, camping stove, a battery-operated radio, water purifier, blankets, first aid kit and a fire extinguisher could all help to save lives.

Checking over the home, to reduce the danger of being crushed from falling furniture, could also be a life-saver. Book cases and other tall heavy furniture should be fastened to walls. Shelves should have a lip at the edge to stop heavy ornaments, food tins and flower pots from being thrown off. Heavy equipment such as computers and televisions should be fastened in position.

On the outside of the house, damaged guttering, brick and stone work and loose roof tiles should be dealt with routinely. Chimney stacks should be checked and kept in sound condition. It is a good idea to read the household insurance policy,

and put into practice any special earthquake precautions that are listed there, and to decide whether to buy earthquake coverage if the policy doesn't already include it.

All members of the family should have an agreement on where to return to, should they become separated during the chaos that follows an earthquake.

1 In Ecuador they take geological risks seriously. The roadsign reads *Geological fault — drive with caution*.

During an earthquake

Many people are injured by breaking glass, falling roof tiles and other bits of masonry as they run out of the house in panic. It is safest to shelter under a large heavy piece of furniture or in a doorway till the shaking stops. Californian children are taught to 'duck and cover' — duck under a table or desk, and cover their head.

People who are already outdoors should stay away from buildings, and keep clear of steep slopes to avoid landslips.

*P*repare to survive

2 School children practising earthquake drill in the town of Parkfield in central California.

3 Below, information panels in telephone directories can give reminders in an emergency.

After an earthquake

Those who live near a coastline should keep away from the shore, to avoid the risk of being swamped by tsunami waves.

The main earthquake may be followed by aftershocks in the hours or days that follow. Buildings that are superficially damaged by the main shock may become dangerous or may collapse during these smaller events. If the home is standing but appears unsafe, it is wisest to check that electricity, gas and other services are turned off, collect emergency supplies, and head for a safer place in the open. It may be difficult to resist the temptation to collect personal possessions from a damaged home, but the decision could make the difference between life and death.

Published with the support of
Telecom Directories Limited.
A subsidiary of Telecom
Corporation of New Zealand

Produced by the Ministry of Civil Defence.

CD CIVIL DEFENCE

Prepare to Survive

1 Learn about the local hazards from the Civil Defence staff at your council.
2 Know your local Civil Defence Warning Signal.
3 Know how to turn off the electricity, gas and water.
4 Prepare a family plan in case you get separated.
5 Know where to get help.

Put together a survival kit.
Check your kit regularly.

Make sure you can find these items in the dark.

If Disaster Strikes
Turn on your radio and listen for instructions.

If you live in an isolated area and need help – display a bed sheet outside to attract attention.

If you have to leave home take these items with you and fill out the Evacuation Card below.
Practise collecting these items together.

Evacuation Card
Fill this in and place it in your front window.

Names _____
This address is _____
We left at _____ am/pm on _____ (date)
We have gone to _____
That address is _____
The phone number there is _____

Before you leave:
Make sure no one is left behind, turn off electricity, gas and water.

71

Index & further reading

Further reading

Earthquakes and Volcanoes by Fiona Allen (1993). Usborne Understanding Geography series.

Eyewitness Guide Volcano by Susanna van Rose (1992). Dorling Kindersley.

The Citizens' Guide to Geologic Hazards by Edward B Nuhfer and others (1993). American Institute of Professional Geologists, 7828 Vance Drive, Suite 103, Arvada, 80003.

Earthquakes and Geological Discovery by Bruce A Bolt (1993). Scientific American Library.

Global Tectonics by P Kearey & J Vine (1990). Blackie Science.

Active Tectonics, Earthquakes, Uplift and Landscape by E A Keller & N Pinter (1996). Prentice Hall.

Earthquakes by B A Bolt (1993) (Newly Revised and Expanded). Freeman.

A Catalogue of British Earthquakes by R M W Musson (1994). Technical Report No.2 WL/94/04, British Geological Survey

Seismicity of the Earth & Related Phenomena by B Gutenberg & C F Richter (2nd Ed 1965). Hafner.

Elementary Seismology by C F Richter (1958). Freeman.